PLOUGHSHARES

Spring 2014 • Vol. 40, No. 1

GUEST EDITOR
Jean Thompson

EDITOR-IN-CHIEF
Ladette Randolph

INTERIM MANAGING EDITOR
Ellen Duffer

FICTION EDITOR
Margot Livesey

POETRY EDITOR
John Skoyles

FOUNDING EDITOR
DeWitt Henry

FOUNDING PUBLISHER
Peter O'Malley

PRODUCTION MANAGER
Akshay Ahuja

MARKETING ASSISTANT
Miriam Cook

EDITORIAL ASSISTANTS
Alexandra Artiano, Abby Travis
& David Weinstein

SENIOR READERS
Sarah Banse, David Goldstein
& Abby Travis

DIGITAL PUBL. ASSISTANT
Jessica Arnold

BLOG EDITOR
Andrew Ladd

COPY EDITOR
Carol Farash

ePUBLISHING CONSULTANT
John Rodzvilla

INTERNS
Gabriella Balza, Sydney Hermanson,
Kim Lester & Gabrielle Tyson

READERS
Emily Avery-Miller | Jana Lee Balish | Doug Paul Case
Marlena Clark | Lindsay D'Andrea | Nicole DiCello | Jennifer Feinberg
Diana Filar | John Francisconi | Colleen Fullin | Joshua Garstka | Kristine Greive
Mark Hengstler | Rachael Inciarte | Ethan Joella | Chelsea Johnston | Kristina
Kopić | Renee Lamine | Mark Lewis | Karen Lonzo | Kristian Macaron | Jean
Mattes | Autumn McClintock | Caitlin McGill | Stephanie Mendoza
Marisela Navarro | June Rockefeller | Wesley Rothman | Charlotte Seley
Alessandra Siraco | Matt Socia | Sarah Stetson | Jordan Stillman
Paige Towers | Ross Wagenhofer | Charles Walker
Caitlin Walls | Leah Welch | Kristen Winstead

ADVISORY BOARD
DeWitt Henry | Alice Hoffman | Ann Leary
Tom Martin | Pam Painter | Janet Silver | Marillyn Zacharis

Ploughshares, a journal of new writing, is guest-edited serially by prominent writers who explore different personal visions, aesthetics, and literary circles. *Ploughshares* is published in April, August, and December at Emerson College: 120 Boylston Street, Boston, MA 02116-4624. Telephone: (617) 824-3757. Web address: pshares.org. E-mail: pshares@pshares.org.

Advisory Editors: Sherman Alexie, Russell Banks, Andrea Barrett, Charles Baxter, Ann Beattie, Madison Smartt Bell, Anne Bernays, Frank Bidart, Amy Bloom, Robert Boswell, Henry Bromell, Rosellen Brown, Ron Carlson, James Carroll, David Daniel, Peter Ho Davies, Madeline DeFrees, Mark Doty, Rita Dove, Stuart Dybek, Cornelius Eady, Martín Espada, B. H. Fairchild, Nick Flynn, Carolyn Forché, Richard Ford, George Garrett, Lorrie Goldensohn, Mary Gordon, Jorie Graham, David Gullette, Marilyn Hacker, Donald Hall, Patricia Hampl, Joy Harjo, Kathryn Harrison, Stratis Haviaras, Terrance Hayes, DeWitt Henry, Edward Hirsch, Jane Hirshfield, Tony Hoagland, Alice Hoffman, Fanny Howe, Marie Howe, Major Jackson, Gish Jen, Justin Kaplan, Bill Knott, Yusef Komunyakaa, Maxine Kumin, Don Lee, Philip Levine, Margot Livesey, Thomas Lux, Gail Mazur, Campbell McGrath, Heather McHugh, James Alan McPherson, Sue Miller, Lorrie Moore, Paul Muldoon, Antonya Nelson, Jay Neugeboren, Howard Norman, Tim O'Brien, Joyce Peseroff, Carl Phillips, Jayne Anne Phillips, Robert Pinsky, Alberto Ríos, Lloyd Schwartz, Jim Shepard, Jane Shore, Charles Simic, Gary Soto, Elizabeth Spires, David St. John, Maura Stanton, Gerald Stern, Mark Strand, Elizabeth Strout, Christopher Tilghman, Richard Tillinghast, Colm Tóibín, Chase Twichell, Jean Valentine, Fred Viebahn, Ellen Bryant Voigt, Dan Wakefield, Derek Walcott, Rosanna Warren, Alan Williamson, Eleanor Wilner, Tobias Wolff, C. D. Wright, Al Young, Kevin Young

Subscriptions (ISSN 0048-4474): $30 for one year (3 issues), $50 for two years (6 issues); $39 a year for institutions. Add $30 a year for international postage ($10 for Canada).

Upcoming: Fall 2014, a fiction issue edited by Percival Everett, will be published in August. Winter 2014-15, a staff-edited poetry and prose issue, will be published in December 2014. Spring 2015, an international poetry issue edited by Neil Astley, will be published in April 2015.

Submissions: The regular reading period is from June 1 to January 15 (postmark and online dates). All submissions sent from January 16 to May 31 will be returned unread. From March 1 to May 15, we also read for our Emerging Writer's Contest. Please see page 216 for editorial and submission policies, or visit our website: pshares.org/submit.

Back-issue, classroom-adoption, and bulk orders may be placed directly through Ploughshares. *Ploughshares* is also available as full-text products from EBSCO, H.W. Wilson, JSTOR, ProQuest, and the Gale Group. Indexed in M.L.A. Bibliography, Humanities International Index, and Book Review Index. Full publishers' index is online at pshares.org. The views and opinions expressed in this journal are solely those of the authors. All rights for individual works revert to the authors upon publication. Ploughshares receives support from the National Endowment for the Arts and the Massachusetts Cultural Council.

Retail distribution by Ingram Periodicals, Media Solutions, Ubiquity, and Disticor Direct in Canada. Printed in the U.S.A. by The Sheridan Press.

Jean Thompson photo by Marion Ettlinger. Elise Juska photo by Dan Bernstein. The image in Peter Rock's story "Go-Between" (and the cover) is by Peter McCollough.

CONTENTS

Spring 2014

Cover: Peter Earl McCollough, *Detail from Untitled Photograph*. Courtesy of the artist.

JEAN THOMPSON
Introduction

First the good news: In spite of every dour pronouncement I've heard over the four decades I've called myself a writer, and probably going even farther back, literature as we know it is not in crisis. Reading is not obsolete. Books are not doomed. Print is not archaic, nor is it likely to become so. Poetry is not dead. Short stories are not dead. Novels are not dead. They are not even sick.

Alarming claims always get more attention, though there have been some legitimate alarms in recent years. The diminishment of paying markets for quality poetry and fiction is one. The economics of publishing haven't become any less brutal, and the trend toward consolidation among the major publishing houses is not particularly author-friendly. Too many books chase too few readers. The digital revolution is here, and for every opportunity it brings, there is also anxiety. All true, all concerning. But I do take it badly when these are seen as signs of the end of days, and when writing of the sort I love (and practice) is dismissed as no longer viable or even possible.

Some perspective: in 1961, Philip Roth wrote, "The American writer in the middle of the 20th century has his hands full in trying to understand, describe, and then make credible much of American reality."

Many writers seemed to agree; the old realistic forms simply would not do now. These writers disassembled conventional structures and put them back together in unexpected ways, the same as you might take the wheels off a car and mount them on the roof or hood. There were a great many stories told in fragments, or with self-conscious narrators who called our attention to the artifice of the whole proceeding. There were books where the lyricism of voice substituted for any real narrative momentum, there were some wildly wonderful creations. That is, sometimes the car went forward, and sometimes it rolled over in a ditch. (I leave the history of language poetry for others to tell.) It was a difficult time to be a writer of fiction in which recognizable events happened to recognizable someones. "You simply can't write stories like that anymore," I was told, and I didn't have any real comeback, because it had never occurred to me that I was doing it all wrong.

What happened? Raymond Carver, for one thing, and his plain-spoken authenticity, his no-fuss minimalism. He was immediately and hugely influential. His mannerisms were easily imitated, if not his artistry. Suddenly, everyone wanted to write like Carver, where before they had wanted to write like French post-structuralists. Richard Ford, Tobias Wolff, Ann Beattie, and many other fine writers claimed our attention. The pendulum lurched. The car found another gear and zoomed away. Ever since, at intervals, new gears have propelled us as the old ones lost their zip.

Art is restless, art is charged with reinventing and reimagining itself at every moment. So I understand the necessity of movement and antimovement. But this history makes me disinclined to believe the worst, most apocalyptic pronouncements about literary culture. For instance, once writing programs established themselves in every nook and cranny of university life, there was a lot of fretting that "the work-shop story" (imposed by groupthink, small-scale, safe, ironic, offering up its tiny epiphanies) would crowd out more original efforts. If there ever was a vogue for such stories, it seems to have passed, or evolved, and the creatures no longer roam the veldts and savannas as they once did. Originals, meanwhile, have gone right on being original.

Recently, I saw a notice for a scholarly lecture about "the new intermodal book." I was not able to determine the precise meaning of *intermodal.* (I confess I did not attend the lecture.) Google thinks it has something to do with transportation systems. But there were clues in the notice, once you got past the lingo—epistemological currents and prem-ises of post-postmodernism and such—that the scholar was focusing on "word-image interactions," that is, books with pictures, as an important "morphing" of contemporary fiction. Ever since scholars reinvented themselves, no longer the fusty guardians and interpreters of tradition, but discoverers and even entrepreneurs of the up-to-the-minute, we have had many such proclamations. If you can wrap your mind around the concept of post-postmodernism, a term that seems ready to burst into spores like a wet mushroom, then I suppose you can understand the need to push and prod and coax the culture into new, exciting trends that have not really happened yet. I have nothing against books with pictures. Like most people, I grew up with them. Everything new is old again.

Two things seem at odds, one being some bedrock of expectations we have from literature, the other being the innovative and revolutionary impulse which disowns all that has gone before. To me, the absolute bedrock of fiction is to make the reader want to know what happens next. And if you want to assemble a pastiche of lists and quotes and lonely paragraphs and call it a novel, well, it's a free country, as we used to say in the days before the Patriot Act. About poetry I am less schooled, but I imagine as a basic that it ought to operate rather like an old-fashioned pinball machine, sending language zipping through the brain and lighting it up, ding ding ding, and finally, Jackpot! Nonfiction: facts matter when it comes to landing airplanes, cancer diagnoses, and court proceedings, and if you persist, even given allowance for memory, subjectivity, artistry, etc., in playing peek-a-boo with your reader as to whether you are being factual, then perhaps what you are writing about does not matter very much.

Ah well. To each their own path. In fact, the thing that gives me hope for the enterprise of writing is the incredible variety and vigor of the terrain. There is more than enough room for vampires in love, for futuristic visions, for collisions between high and low culture, for passionate arguments and counterarguments. Online reading and online publishing have only expanded the reach of words on a page, or the facsimile of a page, and those who want to build their own books now have access to the digital garage. Readers in plenty are still out there, regardless of the fascinations of video games and other entertainments. Reality has hardly eased up in the more than fifty years since Roth's lament; it still generates the kind of headlines that you're sorry you had to see. And writers still grapple or dance with the world we live in, reflect or distort it, embrace or escape it. The short story is still with us, as difficult to kill off as Rasputin. Poetry, that most enduring and subversive of forms, isn't going away any time soon, and novels continue to be part of the national conversation. The human impulse and need to shape words remains.

Nor have the writers included in this issue gotten the message that they are engaged in some quaint or dying craft. Their work has delighted and, even better, surprised me. They come to you from zip codes around the country and from across at least one ocean. They have no mode or method in common, only excellence. I invite you to spend some time with them now.

There is no bad news.

MARK BRAZAITIS
The Rink Girl

Her family moved to town from Omaha on Christmas Eve. Her father and mother are the new managers of the Sherman Ice Arena, which, thanks to the coal-baron millionaire who owns it, is open all year. It is mid-January now, skating season. Half the town goes to the public skate on Saturday afternoon, the experience like walking down aisles of a sold-out show. *Excuse me. Sorry. Hey—watch it!*

Walt waits in the long line to rent skates. Behind the counter is the Rink Girl. She isn't pretty. This is what every boy in the tenth grade says. Acne coats the sides of her face like raindrops on a window. Her brown hair looks oily, and its curls are petals of a wilted flower. Her eyes, however, are a dazzling hazel.

"Size?" she says. She looks him over. "Wait. Aren't you in the geography class before mine?" Geography, a tenth-grade elective. His parents insisted he enroll so he wouldn't be ignorant of the world. "Walt, right?"

"Yeah."

"What size, Walt?"

He tells her and she retrieves a pair of night-blue skates from the shelf behind her. The skates are the newest the rink owns, she says. "The gray ones have been here since 1947. The brown ones? Since the Civil War."

She looks to her left, out the windows of the double doors and onto the rink. Ten minutes after the start of the session, it's packed. Shaking her head, she turns back to him. He hears someone grumble in the line behind him: "What is this, the post office?"

"How much do you like skating?" the Rink Girl whispers, her voice as intimate as a lullaby.

"I like it fine," he says.

"Come back at midnight."

"Is there another public skate?"

"Come back at midnight," she repeats.

He wakes up as if to an alarm. The red numbers of his digital clock radiate the time: 11:42. He fell asleep convinced the Rink Girl wasn't serious about midnight. There's only one way to know for sure, however. He exchanges his pajamas for the clothes on his floor. His house is asleep. Silver, his dog, acknowledges him with three thumps of his tail before closing his eyes again. He steps outside.

The rink isn't more than a mile from his house. Because the night is clear and full of stars and the roads are free of snow and ice, he rides his bike. He makes it to the rink in minutes. But of course the door is locked, and when he taps like a hopeful fool, no one answers. If Brian and Ben could see him now, they would laugh all week. They were supposed to join him at the rink this afternoon, but they watched football instead.

"Hey." He turns to the voice behind him. "You're early." The Rink Girl smiles. In the bright-dark night, in her gray overcoat and bowler hat, she looks like a bohemian detective. She inserts a key into the rink's front-door lock, turns it, and pushes the door in. "After you."

It is darker than night inside. Then it's as light as a party. The Rink Girl calls him over from her spot behind the counter. "Do you want the same boots?" she asks.

"Sorry?"

"The same skates. Do you want the same skates you had on today?"

"Sure," he says.

She places the night-blue skates on the counter. Her own skates are white, with red hearts on the toes. As she laces them up in the lobby, he stares at them. "It was either hearts or skulls," she says. "Next time, I'm going with skulls."

She kills the lights in the lobby and clicks them on in the rink. She pushes open the double doors and leads him to the gate. She snaps it open and draws it in. "Gentlemen first," she says. He isn't prepared for how smooth the ice is—he is used to it being gnawed by a hundred blades—and he finds his feet flying forward and his head plummeting backward.

She catches him under his shoulders. "Careful, cowboy." She rights him with surprising strength. He glides onto the immaculate ice. She moves in front of him with the ease of a bird soaring across the sky, her coat like wings.

He follows her over several laps of the rink before she slows to skate beside him. "What's your story?" she asks.

"What do you mean?"

"Who are you? What do you want to be when you grow up? What's your favorite sin?" She laughs as if she isn't serious. But then she gazes at him as if she is.

He edits his answers so he'll sound cool, adventurous. But she follows up with more questions, and he ends up telling her the truth: His name is Walt Taylor. He is fifteen years old. His best sport is swimming. His favorite class is geography. (He wouldn't have said this before today, but he is convinced of it now.) He doesn't have a girlfriend. He last kissed a girl when he was in the sixth grade. When he was younger, he sometimes practiced kissing on his dog. He doesn't know what his favorite sin is because he feels guilty even when he doesn't sin. He wants to be in the movies. He'd settle for being a newscaster in Cleveland.

"All right," he says, "now you."

Her name is the Rink Girl. No, of course it isn't. But she knows people call her the Rink Girl. She doesn't mind. She loves skating rinks. She loves how they smell. She loves how the Zamboni mows them clean, leaving tiny, shimmering puddles. Her parents, who won a bronze medal in pairs skating at the World Championships a hundred years ago, moved to the United States from Russia when they were in their early twenties in order to join the Skating Sensations tour. This lasted two and a half years. They have been the managers of six rinks, the last outside Omaha.

"What happened in Omaha?" he asks.

"The city couldn't afford to operate the rink anymore. It's a ghost building now."

"That won't happen here."

She shrugs. "Let's hope."

They skate a loop around the rink in silence. "Are you bored yet?" she asks.

"What?" he says.

"Boys tend to get bored with ice skating."

"So you've skated with a lot of boys."

"My brother," she says. "If he doesn't have a stick, a puck, and a net, he doesn't want to be anywhere near a rink."

"What grade is he in?"

"He's in the army."

"In the war?"

She nods. She is silent as she skates.

"I'm not bored," he says.

She says, "You know what my favorite sin is? Disobedience."

"Oh," he says. "So your parents don't know you're here?" He looks around, as if they might be hiding in the shadows.

"They do," she says. "But they don't know *you're* here." She smiles and dashes in front of him. "Catch me," she says.

It's impossible. After they have done a dozen laps, she calls across the rink: "You don't have to go the same direction I'm going." In a louder voice, she says, "Catch me any way you can."

But even when he turns around, she is too skilled and swift for him. He fails even to touch her. Cramping from exhaustion, he leaves the ice. She joins him in the second row of the three-tiered bleachers. Panting, he says, "Trying to…catch you…is like…trying to…catch light."

She touches his knee. He looks at her hand, then at her face. Her dazzling hazel eyes. Her pimples like small pink jewels. Her lips.

Her hand meets his. He squeezes it and she squeezes back.

"This doesn't mean I'm going to kiss you," she says.

She says they ought to leave. "I could probably teach you to be the world's greatest figure skater in the next couple of hours," she says. "But then neither of us would have a reason to come back. You would be on a Wheaties box and I would be the Annie Sullivan of skating teachers."

"Who's Annie Sullivan?" he asks.

"She coached Helen Keller to gold at the '24 Olympics."

Outside, the sky is as luminous as he's ever seen it. She walks up steps to the street and is about to cross. "What about a kiss?" he asks, surprised by his boldness.

She turns around. "Maybe when you catch me," she says. There is a pause. "Hell, that will never happen." She skips down the stairs and plants an ice-cool kiss on his lips. The sensation is like winter's first snowfall. "Goodnight."

On Monday morning in the third-floor hallway at Sherman High School, she doesn't acknowledge Walt's wave. At the door to the geography classroom at the fifth-period bell, he touches her shoulder. She looks at him as if he's a spider's web with which she tangled on a walk in the woods.

At the end of the school day, he walks home, disconsolate. As soon as he steps into the alley off Lye Street, she leaps from behind a green garbage can. He is too happy to be startled. But remembering how she treated him today, he narrows his eyes. "What's up?" he says.

"I know I ignored you at school," she says. "But I did it for your own good."

"What do you mean?"

"If your friends knew you liked the Rink Girl, you wouldn't hear the end of their teasing."

"I can handle them," he says, although without confidence.

"Besides, it's easier this way," she says. "We can concentrate on school when we're at school."

"And after school, we can do what we want."

"No, we have to do our homework."

"Are you serious?" The disappointment in his voice is as evident as a tuba in an orchestra of harps.

Softly, she says, "My parents don't want me to grow up to be the Rink Woman. And they don't want me to join the army like my brother. They're thinking doctor, lawyer, CEO of the world. So they want me to spend every afternoon and evening between Sunday and Friday in the company of books, calculators, and computers."

"I see," Walt says.

"So Saturday night is all we have." She pauses. "Saturday night and now."

She pulls him toward her. Squatting behind the green garbage can, they touch each other's ears and tangle tongues.

At the rink on Saturday night, she dazzles him with what she can do.

"What was that?" he asks. "A double axel?"

"Is that an official jump?" she says.

"I think so."

"I never had a lesson in my life—my parents were always too busy to teach me—so I don't know any of the real jumps or spins or moves. I've made up my own. I'll teach them all to you. This one I call the Floating Phantom."

She dives into the air, her body—he swears—horizontal to the ice before she rolls over as if on an invisible bed and, with her arms in front of her like a sleepwalker, returns to the cold surface.

"This one I call the Sit-Up." She jumps into the air, kicks both legs straight in front of her, and curls up to touch her toes before sticking her legs back on the ice.

"And this I just call Crazy." She leaps into the air, somersaults, and lands without falling, without even trembling.

"Wow," he says. "Wow."

"Which one do you want to learn first?"

He considers. "How about we begin with you teaching me how to skate backward?"

She taps her lips. "Boring," she says. "But all right." She steps in front of him, facing him. "Put your hands up like you're touching a wall."

When he does, she puts her hands in his. Neither of them is wearing gloves. But if his hands were cold, they are no longer. For years when he sees a couple standing like this, facing each other, palms pressed together, fingers interlocked, he will remember her, and he will feel sweetly disoriented, as if he had time-traveled.

Gently, she pushes into him, instructing him how to move his skates like he's using them to draw ovals in the ice.

After several minutes, she says, "I think you have it," and she gives him a push and he glides backward, as if on air, to the end of the rink.

The Rink Girl does not insist he practice his skating, but if he is to become as good as she is, or even half as good as she is—if he is to impress her at all—he must practice. So he comes to the public sessions on Wednesday and Thursday nights, fighting past mad-dashing eight-year-olds in hockey masks and trios of linked-armed twelve-year-old girls and divorced men and women on first dates as awkward as their skating.

On occasion, he glimpses the Rink Girl at a desk in the small office behind the rental skates, a textbook spread in front of her, a pen or pencil in her hand. Always, he lingers, wanting her to see him and beam, wanting to leap over the counter, slide up beside her, whisper into her brown hair.

During a school assembly in mid-March, he finds himself, by luck of the way homeroom classes occupy the rows of seats in the auditorium, sitting beside her. Police officers occupy the stage, railing against drugs or graffiti or something else subversive. She won't look at him, won't acknowledge him with anything even so small as a smile. He is terrified of making such a move himself, worried she will respond in a manner as cold as the ice on which she thrills him.

"Say no to temptation," he hears a police officer say. "Say no to impulsiveness, to wildness, to irrational behavior. Say no, no, no."

He feels his hand fill, remarkably, with hers. She leans over to him, kisses his ear, whispers, "Say yes, yes, yes."

As a skater, Walt isn't improving as quickly as he wants. He skates backward now, but he is far from mastering even the move she calls the Semi-Sane, which is a leap, a landing on two feet, and a spin into a backward skate. "Watch," she says. When she does it, it seems as simple as playing hopscotch. But when he tries to imitate her, he falls.

"Again," she says.

He falls.

"Again."

He falls.

"Again."

He falls. He falls. He falls. He falls. He falls. He falls.

He succeeds.

"Again."

He falls.

"Again."

He is in love, but no one knows it. He confides in no one. Not his parents. Not his older brother. Not Brian and Ben. To tell, he thinks, might be to awaken him from his dream or to have it trivialized with "Isn't that sweet" or with teasing or with (in Ben's and Brian's case) rude remarks about her pimples or her oily hair or the way she smells of old skates.

"Again."

He falls.

"Again."

He falls.

"Again."

He falls.

"I'll show you something special if you do it right."

He succeeds.

In the center of the ice, she lifts her blue sweater slowly. Thinking she is going to show him her breasts, his heart chugs like a manic

choo-choo train. But she stops short, the bottom of the sweater a bar-
ricade. Now he sees her revelation: a red scar beginning at her navel
and shooting like an angry bolt toward her breastbone.

"What happened?" he asks.

"I was doing a combination of the Buddha and the Ballerina. My
blades had just been sharpened. They might as well have been ninja
knives."

"It's amazing."

"You were probably hoping I'd show you my tits."

"I mean, it's amazing that you made a mistake. I've never seen
you—"

"Who said anything about making a mistake? I tried to do a mash
up of two irreconcilable moves. It's like dancing over the canyon of a
paradox."

"Excuse me?"

"You did want to see my tits, didn't you?"

God yes, he thinks.

"Well, it's your lucky night."

In the beginning of June, Walt turns sixteen. This is good fortune. He
needs an automobile because his summer job, to which he applied nine
months earlier, is at a YMCA overnight camp in Bellefontaine, Ohio,
four hours from Sherman. The automobile wasn't originally a necessity.
He'd planned to spend his entire summer on the campgrounds. But if
he wants to see the Rink Girl, which is akin to asking if he wants to live,
he'll need to drive back from Bellefontaine every Saturday.

Each employee of Camp Belle is allowed one night off a week. Naturally, everyone wants Saturday night. Seniority dictates who is assigned
what day, however. As a junior counselor, Walt sees he will be stuck
with Tuesdays and Thursdays. On his first day at camp, he thinks about
quitting. But his parents—his accursed parents—have opted to trade
houses over the summer with a couple from Vallebona, Italy. He has
nowhere to stay in Sherman.

In exchange for their Saturday nights, he surrenders to his fellow
counselors his baseball glove, his fishing rod, his iPod. He doesn't miss
any of it, except, perhaps, his baseball glove when, playing left field
during the camper-counselor softball game, he catches a fly ball with
his bare palm.

Because he is permitted to leave camp after dinner on Saturday, he has no problem arriving at the rink by midnight. The return trip's timeline proves tighter. He leaves the rink as the sun slips its first light over the horizon like a lover sliding a letter under a door. He crushes the gas pedal to make it back by Sunday breakfast, which, fortunately, begins at 9:30.

Over the succeeding days, he catnaps when he can in order to recuperate the sleep he lost in staying up all night. By the time Saturday comes again, he is fully rested. He doesn't tell the Rink Girl about the lengths he goes to see her. He doesn't want her to think he's as lovesick as he is.

The Rink Girl spends her summer weekdays at a series of science and math camps in Cleveland and Columbus. Sometimes he hears her mumbling what sound like formulas or Latin mottoes. *Supra glaciem stemus, cum corde ignis.*

She teaches him the Slam, which is a series of short jumps followed by a high jump. She teaches him the Slow Mirror, in which one side of his body repeats the movements of the other. She teaches him the Backward Peek-a-Boo, in which he skates backward and pokes his head between his legs to see where he's going.

Despite the scoreboard above the east end of the rink with its red-numbered clock, dawn always surprises them. At first light, they kiss with the fury of hummingbirds stealing dew from the flowers of a butterfly bush.

On the Saturday night before the beginning of school, when Walt is back from camp, she isn't at the rink. In her place is a note with his name: *Had to leave town. Left the door open. The ice is yours.*

But without her, the ice feels—and he realizes how odd it is to think this way—cold. The rink feels cavernous and lonely, like a ship abandoned at sea. He drifts around the ice like a shipwrecked sailor hoping to find an island. He leaves after less than an hour, then stays up all night, wondering where she is and what might be wrong.

On the first day of school, he stands beside the main entrance to Sherman High like a soldier. He doesn't care if she doesn't speak to him. He only wants to see her. For the past twenty-four hours, he has done nothing but worry—irrationally, he knows—that she is gone forever, off to bless another rink in another town, to turn another boy's

Saturday nights into magic. The last bell rings, and he slinks inside the building and slouches to his homeroom.

But at the change of classes before third period, he sees her at the end of the hall. He is so relieved he fails to realize they are approaching each other with the speed of speed skaters. They collide, and she is sobbing a hurricane. "What's wrong?"

"My brother," she says.

"What happened? He didn't...Is he...?"

He feels her nod against his shoulder. Her tears are ferocious.

There is an audience around them. But the bell rings, and the hallway empties.

"We had to meet the body," she says. "We buried him in the National Cemetery in Virginia."

"I'm sorry," he says. After a moment, he adds, "I wish I had more to say."

"There isn't more to say."

At school, it is impossible to pretend they aren't boyfriend and girlfriend. But perhaps owing to her brother's death, news of which everyone seems to have heard, they are left alone. They eat their lunches at the far end of the football field, in a corner where the grass is softest. They walk home together every day. In the wake of her brother's death, there is a solemnity to their conversations. Even their Saturday nights on the ice assume a mournful aura, the jumps, spins, and moves she teaches him bearing such names as Cerement ("a shroud," she explains helpfully), Heaven's Door, and, defiantly, Death Be Not Proud.

One Saturday night, she gives him a pair of ice skates, black with red eyelets. She doesn't say to whom they belonged, but he knows. They fit perfectly.

"I think it's time," she says at the beginning of October.

"Time?"

"To do a duet."

His role is simple. He skates forward, from one end of the rink to the other. She moves around him like water moves around rocks in a rippling stream. "Now backward," she says. He skates backward, and she flies around him, a predator about to devour him. No, only a butterfly looking to land.

Which she does, in his arms. "I feel better," she says.

*

In the middle of October, she invites him to have dinner at her house. From outside, her house looks ordinary: faded brick, ornamental wooden shutters with chipping white paint, a covered front porch with a pair of rocking chairs. Inside, he discovers a long hallway whose walls, top to bottom, are lined with photographs of her brother. "My parents say if the photos went halfway around the world," the Rink Girl whispers, "it would be too short a distance by half."

Presently, her parents come to meet him. Her father is tall and burly, with a beard that could hide a small child. Her mother is short and thin, with dyed orange hair in the style of a broom end. "I see you've met our son," she says. Walt looks around, as if there might be someone else in the room. But of course there is: the walls are alive.

"I'm sorry for your loss," he says.

But they appear not to have heard him. "Handsome, isn't he?" her mother says.

Her father adds, "And smart as a scientist."

Her parents have already eaten—or perhaps they aren't hungry—because after a minute more of polite talk, they excuse themselves and disappear. The Rink Girl waves him deeper into the house, into the kitchen, where she pulls pots and pans from cabinets. "What would you like to eat?" she asks. "Name anything."

"Anything?"

"Anything."

You, he wants to say.

"I don't know. Well." *Right now I'd like to taste the right corner of your mouth.* "Sea bass with rice pilaf, carrots au gratin, and a Caesar salad."

"Excellent," she says. "Next time, I'll know. Tonight we'll have peanut butter and jelly sandwiches. Any objections?"

He has none.

As they eat their sandwiches with a side of applesauce in lunch-size containers, he says, "Where did your parents go?"

She shrugs. "They haven't been here in anything more than body since my brother died. If I were a different kind of daughter, I would take advantage of the situation by, I don't know, hauling you upstairs and losing my virginity to you under the poster of Amelia Earhart on my ceiling."

"You have a poster of Amelia Earhart on your ceiling?"

She looks at him askance. "That's what you found interesting about what I just said?"

On the ice, he learns, or half learns, or watches her demonstrate, the Rabbit, the Monkey, the Horse, and the other nine signs of the Chinese zodiac.

"Someday," she says, "I'll teach you the Big O."

"What's the Big O?"

She only smiles.

Several times she tries to sneak him into her house—"to introduce you to Amelia Earhart," in her winking words—when she thinks her parents aren't home, but one or both are always present. One time, her parents are entertaining the Medev family from Moscow. If the Rink Girl's father is ursine, Lev Medev—tall, bearded, and with a girth so large he might have eaten a bear—is doubly so. He is the owner of the Moscow Circus on Ice, which is in town to do a one-night show. The Medevs have a son, whom the Rink Girl's parents have been encouraging her to spend time with.

"I hope he's twice as ugly as his old man," Walt tells her, feeling jealousy burn so hot in him he could cook a four-course meal on his chest.

"I thought he would be" is all the Rink Girl says in reply.

She likes him. Damn it all. Could she like him more than she likes me? Please, God, no. Now Walt's chest blazes like the center of the sun.

The next Saturday night, the Rink Girl brings a pair of blankets onto the ice.

"Don't pretend you don't know what these are for," she says.

"Oh," he says.

"Close," she says. "The Big O." She laughs and pulls him down toward the unforgettable.

"This is it," he says afterward—or after the third afterward. "This is the summit of my existence on earth."

"Time to move to Mars," she says, kissing him again.

But it is she who might be moving. The Medevs have offered her parents the chance to manage their five rinks in Moscow, as well as the amusement park next door to a prison that briefly housed Aleksandr Solzhenitsyn. "There's a ride called One Minute in the Life of Ivan Denisovich," she says. She looks him over. "You don't think I'm funny?"

"I know you're funny," says Walt. "But I don't know who Ivan Denisovich is. And I can't stand the thought of you moving to Moscow."

"My parents haven't been happy since Leo died," she says. "They might see this as a chance to start over—to be reborn where they were born."

They live as if she might leave tomorrow. Saturday nights at the rink become every night at the rink. Some mornings, Walt doesn't know how he manages to rise from his bed. He is deliciously, deliriously exhausted. The holidays come. Halloween. Thanksgiving, Christmas. At midnight on each, he is at the rink.

On New Year's Eve, she tells him her parents have decided they won't be moving to Moscow after all. They celebrate by skating the New Year's Toast, the New Year's Resolution, and Auld Lang Syne. The latter is the easiest. They stand next to each other, wrap their arms around each other's shoulders, and sway.

The next night when Walt arrives at the rink, he sees a pair of two-by-fours nailed across the front entrance. Something awful must have happened inside, he thinks. A gas leak. A burst pipe. A hockey player gone berserk with his stick. But the Rink Girl, behind him now, says, "The rink is closed. The owner is tearing it down to build condos."

Walt turns to her. Her tone tells him she is serious. But he cannot refrain from asking, as if out of an obligation to hope, "Are you joking?"

"The owner told my parents the rink is too expensive to maintain," she says. "He blames it on global warming and sixty-degree winter days."

"But he's creating global warming with his coal. If he would shut down his coal mines, he could keep his rink." The world suddenly seems sinister and doomed. "What happens now?"

She shakes her head. "Moscow," she says. "We leave in three days."

Global warming has taken the evening off. Walt's breath pours out of him as thick as smoke from a coal-fired power plant. What world will he be living in when the Rink Girl is gone? "What? You can't be serious. Are you serious?"

"I would love to be joking."

"You don't have to move," he says. "You can stay here. You can finish high school in Sherman. I'll talk to my parents. You can live with us."

She smiles softly, and he knows it's a prelude to words he doesn't want to hear. "I thought of this," she says. "I thought of a hundred solutions." Her breath fills the air between them. "My parents would miss me too much. Because of what happened to my brother, they want me close."

They walk around the rink, checking windows, checking doors. But nothing gives, nothing opens. They come to the last door, on the edge of the forest at the back of the rink. He kicks it with his black winter boots. He punches it with his bare hands. Bang. Bang. Bang. He finds a brick behind him and smashes it against the wood. Bang. Bang. Bang. He tries his boots again, the brick again. Bang. Bang. Bang. Bang-bang-bang. He drops to his knees.

"I guess no one's home," she says.

He turns. She is at the edge of the woods. A step backward, and she would be swallowed whole by the oak and maple trees. "Fate isn't our friend," she says with a resignation he has never heard from her. "But who marries her high-school sweetheart nowadays anyway?"

"Half the people in this town," he says, sweeping his hands over the dark wood.

"How happy are they?"

"A thousand times happier than I'll be when you're gone."

On their last night together, the Rink Girl proposes they go with their skates to Murderer's Cove on Sky Lake, where the ice is frozen solid. In the twenties and thirties, Murderer's Cove hosted criminal activity ranging from bootlegging to assassination. Or so local legend goes. Now it's a refuge for teenage lovers who lack a private place to crawl into each other's bodies.

The sky is full of stars, as if, from Acamar to Zubeneschamali, they had thrown back the curtain of night to spy on love's last ice dance. He watches the Rink Girl skate across the cove. When she is at the far end, barely visible against a background of pine trees, he skates toward her with a rage he wouldn't have imagined himself capable of. She is facing the trees, her back to him, when he slices to a stop behind her. "Why aren't you furious at the world?" His voice is half accusatory, half perplexed. "Why aren't you as sad as I am?"

But when she turns to him, he sees she is crying, and not gently. "Oh," he says, embarrassed and strangely relieved. They fall into each other. He slides his arms into her coat and around her waist. He pulls her toward him.

"What are we going to do?" she asks.

"Run away with me," he says.

"I wish I could."

"What would it take to convince you?" he asks. "I'll do anything. I'll walk home on my skates. I'll sing all night to the stars." He pauses. "Wait," he says. "I know. I'll show you I can do the most difficult jump you ever tried to teach me." He pushes back from her, onto the starlit cove. "No, I'll do an even harder jump. I'll do the jump you only spoke to me about. What did you call it? The End of the World, right?"

"It's impossible to do an End of the World," she says. "Even I can't do it. You haven't even done a Mini Apocalypse."

"You'll see," he says. "If you say you'll run away with me, I'll do it." The energy of superheroes flows in his veins; he feels he could leap and grab hold of a star. He isn't going to lose her. He's going to do the impossible and they are going to live together forever, their lives always sweet, always delicious.

"If I do it, will you run away with me?"

She nods, a nearly invisible gesture.

"Promise?"

This time there is conviction: "I promise."

"All right," he says. He skates up to her, cups her cheeks, kisses her. "Here goes."

He skates to the center of the cove, fifty feet from her, before halting and swirling around. She is gray against a black background, but she is all the color of his life. He skates toward her with a power he has never possessed. His skates feel like they are barely touching the ice. He moves fast, faster. Ten feet from her, he soars, streaking toward the stars. He does a complete twist and a half, and he is still climbing, like a roaring rocket. He dips his head toward the ice and curls his skates toward the sky. Presently, his skates fall and his head rises, a delirious somersault—and another! Now he is coming down clean. He anticipates her joy, and his, and how their happiness will see them past hardship and doubt, will outburn the stars.

His skates strike the ice straight and perfect. He lifts his arms in triumph, but at the same time, he feels the ice give and open around him. He plummets like a stone.

Years pass, and every breath without her is like ice water in his lungs.

ERIN BELIEU

Fathers Never Answer

A basket in the shape of
a sunflower—

still hanging on
your bedroom wall.

You made it in school.

You loved it so much
you wouldn't stop

making it. Or couldn't
stop. We don't agree,

on what you said.
But I was your favorite.

I thought, What kind of boy
makes such a basket?

Professional looking, all
tight and golden, hanging

on your bedroom wall.
You said

you couldn't stop
making it, weaving it—

however it is you
make a basket—

or wouldn't stop. Even
when they threatened

you with the school for
"retarded boys,"

because you didn't
stop. This was back

then, when parents
said things like that.

A different story, what
we used to do.

But I never forgot.

I thought, Remarkable.
Why wouldn't he

just stop?

ERIN BELIEU

Someone Asks, What Makes This Poem American?

and I answer by driving around, which seems
to me the most American of activities, up there
with waving the incendiary dandelion of sparklers
or eating potato salad with green specks of relish,
the German kind, salad of immigrants, of all
the strange pickled bits we carry
over from other places, like we did on Easter
mornings in Nebraska, stuffing our Sunday
shoes full of straw so that either Jesus
or the Easter Bunny could leave us small,
bullet-shaped candies in honor of what, I was
never quite sure. Where do such customs
come from? Everywhere!
           American-ness is everywhere,
wedged into everything, is best when driving
around a frowzy gulf coast city with its terrific
mini-marts like Bill's, the very best of all marts!
UN of toasted boat rats and boys from the projects
revving their hoopties; of biscuit-shaped ladies who
penny their scratch cards and hold up the line;
where Panama from Panama commands
the counter, and Mr. Bud, the camel-faced man,
offers every kid a sweetie, producing a jar
of petrified lollies from a shelf also
displaying an array of swirly glassed pipes
and Arthurian bongs; where Raoul the Enforcer
idles at the back, packing since the incident
in the parking lot last summer.
                    Of course, people
here have their discontents: the artists save
what tips they don't snort and always mean
to leave for New York or Seattle, though I tell
them both drizzle like November half the time.

So I say, No! That's un-American. We need
our artists everywhere, not scrunched up
in one or two rarefied spots
which makes their parties anxious, and Milosz
says artists come from everywhere, from everyplace,
the capital and the provinces, to keep
the body healthy or else end up like seventeenth-
century Hapsburgs or German Shepherds
listing with hip dysplasia. So I'm circling
the swampy taint of this Southern city, choosing
art, choosing to be American, actively pursuing
that fabled happiness when the alternatives
present themselves, which is my obligation,
both legislator and witness to Bill's
Mini Mart and Mike's Chinese Grocery
and the hungry citizens queuing up
in front of Jenny's Lunchbox, waiting
on line for a pile of cheese grits to start
this day, placing them firmly for the moment
in the happiness column. Because what's more
American than a full stomach on a sunny morning?
What more than this fat-assed acceleration,
driving with the windows cranked down?

ERIN BELIEU
   Energy Policy

This practical kid, born
Capricorn, actuary of the stars,

he's planning my death,
sure of the thermodynamic heaven

he's invented. Because energy
must go somewhere in this system,

in his I'll be repurposed as a tree.
And this comforts me, as no discount

coupons for paradise ever could.
Finally fitting, I'll meet my zero as

the absolute, container of soot buried
at a sapling's root. An organized boy,

he considers all options, which tree to
choose. I haggle for the ornamental—

jazz hands of a Jacaranda,
Fire Thorn to match my hair—

but am dismissed.
He insists on something sturdy:

What lives forever? Then, revising,
Or closest to? Next comes

the issue of where, harder
to answer, as Sequoias don't grow in

Nebraska. *Let's put,* he says, *a pin
in that.* It's his meeting, so we move

on to scenarios, the portrait he'll nail
to my trunk, a bench to sit on when

he comes to talk with me. But what kind
of bench? There's much to discuss with

this faithful child, who knows better than
to bet on the equilibrium, watching

ice in his glass, disordered by degree,
the first share holder in my entropy.

DAN CHAON
What Happened to Us?

Rusty Bickers went walking through the fields at dusk, Rusty Bickers with a sadness and nobility that only Joseph could see. Joseph dreamed of Rusty Bickers at the kitchen table, eating Captain Crunch cereal before bedtime, his head low, lost in thought; Rusty Bickers, silent but awake beneath the blankets on his cot, his hands moving in slow circles over his own body, whispering "Shh…shhh…hush now"; Rusty Bickers standing in the morning doorway of the kitchen, watching Joseph's family as they ate their breakfast, his shaggy hair hanging lank about his face, his long arms dangling from slumped shoulders, his eyes like someone who had been marched a long way to a place where they were going to shoot him.

Joseph heard his mother's bright voice ring out: "It's about time you got up, Rusty!"

Joseph was eight years old, and Rusty was fourteen—an orphan, a foster boy. All that summer, Rusty slept on a folding bed in Joseph's room, so Joseph knew him better than anybody.

Rusty was beginning to grow a man's body. His legs were long and coltish, his feet too big, hair was growing under his arms and around his groin. He had his own tapes, which he listened to through enormous spaceman headphones. He had a souvenir ashtray from the Grand Canyon. He had some books, and photographs of his dead family, and newspaper clippings.

Sometimes, late at night, when Rusty thought that Joseph was asleep, he would slip into Joseph's bed. He curled his long body against Joseph's smaller one, and Joseph stayed still. Rusty put his arm around Joseph as if Joseph were a stuffed animal. Joseph could feel Rusty quivering—he was crying, and his tears fell sharply onto Joseph's bare back. Rusty's arm tightened, pulling Joseph closer.

Rusty's family—his mother, father, and two younger brothers—had died in a fire. Some people, some of Joseph's older cousins, for example, some of them whispered that they heard that Rusty had started the fire himself. Anyway, he was weird, they said. *Psycho.* They stayed away from him.

Before Rusty had come to live with them, Joseph's father was in a terrible accident. He had been working as an electrician on a construction site when a roof collapsed. Joseph's father and his father's best friend, Billy Merritt, fell through three floors. Billy Merritt died instantly. Joseph's father broke both legs, and his right arm was severed. His fall had been softened because he landed on Billy Merritt.

Now Joseph's father had a prosthetic arm, which he was learning to use. The prosthesis looked like two hooks, which his father could clamp together. For example, he was learning how to grasp a fork and lift it to his lips. Eventually, he would be able to turn the pages of a book, or pick up a pin.

There had been a settlement for his father's injury, a large sum of money. The very first thing Joseph's father did was to go and speak with the people at County Social Services. He wanted to take in a foster boy, he said. This had been one of his dreams, something he'd always wanted to do. When he was a teenager, he had been sent away to a home for delinquent boys. After a while, he ran away from that place and joined the Navy. But he still vividly remembered that terrible time of his life.

Joseph's father loved Rusty Bickers. Rusty's story was so sad that perhaps it made the father feel better. He felt that he could help Rusty somehow. He wanted to provide an atmosphere of Love and Happiness.

There was so much money! Joseph had no idea *how* much, but it seemed bottomless. His father bought a new car, and a pool table, and a large screen TV; his mother got her teeth fixed; they began to plan an addition to the house, with a family room and a bedroom for Rusty.

When they went to town, to the big store at the mall, Joseph and his brother and sister and Rusty were allowed to pick out a toy—anything they wanted. While their father looked at tools and electronic devices, Rusty and Joseph and Joseph's younger sister, Cecilia, would lead the baby, Tom, through the rows of toys: the pink and glittery aisle for girls; the mysterious and bookish aisle of games and puzzles; the aisle of action figures and toy weapons and matchbook cars; the aisle of baby stuff—rattles and soft-edged educational devices that looked like dashboards, things that spoke or giggled when you pulled a string. Rusty wandered the aisle of sports stuff, the aisle of BB guns and real bows and arrows, as Joseph and his siblings chased one another. The children could have anything they wanted: the idea almost overcame them.

"Nobody knows what they want, not really," Rusty Bickers said, sometimes, when they were in bed at night. Joseph didn't know whether Rusty had made this up, or whether he was quoting some movie or song. He said this when he was talking about the future. He was thinking about becoming a drummer in a rock band, but he worried that it might be pointless, living out in western Nebraska. He thought that maybe he should live in New York or LA, but he was worried that if he was in such places, the black kids would be always trying to beat him up.

"They hate white people," Rusty told Joseph. "All they want to do is fight you."

Rusty had met black people. He had lived with some black boys in a group home, and he'd had a black teacher.

Joseph hadn't yet seen a black person, though he wanted to. There was a cartoon on TV called *Fat Albert and the Cosby Kids,* about a group of black children who lived in a junkyard. This was Joseph's favorite show, and he longed to make friends with a black child. He hoped that the child would teach him how to talk in that funky way.

"You can't *make friends* with them," Rusty said, scornfully. "All they want to do is kick your ass."

Joseph was silent and thoughtful.

But Rusty didn't even seem to notice. He was thinking of where he would like to go, if he could go somewhere. He leaned back, playing drums on the air above his head.

It was a summer of parties. They were happy times, Joseph remembered later. Friday. Saturday. People would begin to wander in around six or so, bringing coolers full of icy beer and pop, talking loudly—Joseph's uncles and aunts and cousins, his father's old friends from work and their wives and kids—thirty, forty people sometimes. They would barbecue, and there would be corn on the cob, bowls of potato chips and honey-roasted peanuts, slices of cheese and salami, pickled eggs and jalapeños. Music of Waylon Jennings, Willie Nelson, Crystal Gayle. Some people dancing.

Their house was about a mile outside of town. The kids would play outdoors, in the backyard and the large stubble field behind the house.

Dusk seemed to last for hours, and when it was finally dark, they would sit under the porch light, catching thickly buzzing june bugs and moths, or even an occasional toad who hopped into the circle of light, tempted by the halo of insects that floated around the bare orange light bulb next to the front door.

Rusty hardly ever joined in their games. Instead, he would stake out some corner of the yard, or even a chair inside the house, sitting, quietly observing.

Who knew what the adults were doing? They played cards and gossiped. There were bursts of laughter, Aunt DeeDee's high, fun-house cackle rising above the general mumble; they sang along with the songs. After he got drunk, Joseph's father would go around touching the ladies on the back of the neck with his hook, surprising them, making them scream. Sometimes he would take off his arm and dance with it. Sometimes he would cry about Billy Merritt.

The nights grew late. Empty beer cans filled the trash cans and lined the counter tops. The younger children fell asleep in rows on the beds. If he was still awake, Joseph would sometimes gaze out the window, out to where the last remaining adults stood in a circle in the backyard, whispering and giggling, passing a small cigarette from hand to hand. Joseph was eight and wasn't supposed to know what was going on.

But Rusty told him.

At first, Joseph didn't want to believe it. Joseph had mostly heard frightening things about drugs—that wicked people sometimes put LSD in Halloween candy, to make the children go crazy; that if you took Angel Dust, you would try to kill the first person you saw; that dope pushers sometimes came around playgrounds and tried to give children marijuana, and that, if this happened, you should run away and tell an adult as soon as possible.

Rusty had smoked pot; he had also accidentally taken LSD, which someone had given to him in a chocolate bar.

Joseph wasn't sure he believed this either. The depth of Rusty's experience, of his depravity, seemed almost impossible.

Later, when Joseph's parents were out, Joseph and Rusty went through their dresser drawers. They found copies of pornographic magazines in Joseph's father's T-shirt drawer, at the very bottom; in his mother's bra-and-panty drawer, they found a small baggie full of what Rusty said was marijuana.

Rusty took a little for himself, and Joseph nearly started crying.

"Don't tell," Rusty said to him. "You're not going to tell, are you? You know your mom and dad could get in trouble with the police if they ever got caught."

"I won't tell," Joseph whispered.

Joseph's father seemed like a regular father, except for his arm. Sometimes, on Saturdays after breakfast, Joseph and his father and Rusty would drive up into the hills with Joseph's father's 10 gauge rifles. Joseph's father lined up beer cans and mayonnaise jars and such along a fence, and they would shoot at them. Joseph's father could not hold the gun well enough to aim it himself, but he showed Joseph and Rusty how.

The first time Rusty took the gun, his hands were shaking. "Have you ever handled a gun before, son?" Joseph's father said, and Rusty slowly shook his head.

Joseph's father showed Rusty where to hold his hands, how the butt of the gun fit against his shoulder. "OK, OK," Joseph's father said. He stooped behind Rusty, his chin right next to Rusty's ear. "Can you see through the cross hairs? Right where the lines meet?"

Joseph watched as his father and Rusty took careful aim, both their bodies poised for a moment. When the mayonnaise jar burst apart, Joseph leapt up. "You hit it!" he cried, and Rusty turned to him, eyes wide, his mouth slightly open in quiet wonder.

Joseph's mother was waiting with lunch when they got home. She made hamburgers and corn on the cob.

She seemed to Joseph like a typical mother. She was slightly overweight, and bustled, and was cheerful most of the time. When Rusty first came, she would sometimes give him hugs, but he would always become rigid and uncomfortable. After a time, she stopped hugging him. Instead, she would simply rest her hand on his shoulder, or on his arm. Rusty wouldn't look at her when she did this, but he didn't move away either. Joseph thought of what he was learning about plants at school. They drank in sunlight, as their food; they breathed, though you couldn't see it. He thought of this as he watched Rusty sit there, with Joseph's mother's hand on his shoulder. Her hand briefly massaged his neck before she took it away, and Joseph could see the way

Rusty's impassive expression shuddered, the way his eyes grew very still and far away.

Rusty stood at the edge of the backyard and stared out into the distance: the fields, lined with telephone poles; the grasshopper oil wells, gently nodding their sleepy heads. At the edge of the horizon, a ridge of hills rose from the flatland, and Rusty watched them, though there was nothing there. Joseph sat on the back steps and watched what Rusty watched, wondered what Rusty was wondering. After a time, Rusty turned to glance at Joseph. Rusty's face was solemn, stiff with the weight of his thoughts.

"What are you staring at?" Rusty said, and Joseph shrugged.

"Nothing," he said.

"Come over here," Rusty said, and when Joseph did, Rusty didn't say anything for a while. "Hm," he said, considering Joseph's face. "Do you know what would happen if a kid like you got sent to a foster home?"

"No." And Joseph breathed as Rusty's eyes held him, without blinking.

"They do really nasty things to the little kids. And if you try to scream, they put your own dirty underwear in your mouth, to gag you." He stared at Joseph, as if he was imagining this.

Then, abruptly, Rusty gestured at the sky. He pointed. "You see that?" he said. "That's the evening star." He put his palms firmly over Joseph's ears and tilted Joseph's head, swiveling it as if it were a telescope. "You see it now? It's right...there!" And he drew a line with his finger from Joseph's nose to the sky.

Joseph nodded. He closed his eyes. He could feel the cool, claylike dampness of Rusty's palm against his head. The sound of Rusty's hands against his ears was like the whispering inside a shell. "I see it," Joseph said softly.

Sometimes, they all seemed so happy. Here they were, watching TV in the evening, Joseph's mother sitting on his father's lap in the big easy chair, laughing at some secret joke, his mother blushing. Here they were, camping at the lake, roasting marshmallows on sharpened sapling sticks over a campfire; Joseph and Cecilia climbing on their father's shoulders out in the lake and jumping into the water, as if he were a diving board; baby Tom running along the sand naked, laughing as their mother pretended to chase him.

At night, Joseph and Rusty would wade along the edge of the shore with a flashlight, catching crawdads. Rusty wasn't afraid of their pinchers. He would grin hard, letting them dangle like jewelry clamped to the lobes of his ears.

Joseph didn't know what the feeling was that filled him up in such moments. It was something about the way the flashlight's beam made a glossy bowl of light beneath the water; the way, under the beam, everything was clear and distinct—the bits of floating algae and tiny water animals, the polished stones and sleepy minnows flashing silver and metallic blue, the crawdads, sidling backward with their claws lifted warily. It was the sound of his parents' voices in the distance, as they sat around the campfire, the echoing waver as their father began to sing. Rusty was a silhouette against the slick, blue-black stretch of lake, and Joseph could see that the sky wasn't like a ceiling. It was like water too, deep water, depth upon depth, vast beyond measure. And this was something Joseph found beautiful. And he loved his young mother and father, laughing in the distance, and Cecilia and baby Tom, asleep in their tent, already dreaming—and Rusty himself, standing there silently in the dark. He was filled with a kind of awed contentment, which he thought must be happiness.

Later, deep in his sleeping bag in the tent, Joseph could hear his parents talking. Their voices were low, almost underneath the crackling of the fire, but he found that if he listened hard he could understand.

"I don't know," his mother was saying. "How long does it take to get over something like that?"

"He's all right," Joseph's father said. "He's a good kid. He just needs to be left alone. I don't think he wants to talk about it."

"Oh," his mother said, and breathed heavily. "I can't even imagine, you know? I think…What if I lost all of you like that? I don't see how I could go on. I'd kill myself, I really would."

"No you wouldn't," Joseph's father said. "Don't say stuff like that."

And then they were silent. Joseph looked over to where Rusty was lying and saw that Rusty was awake too. The tent walls glimmered with firelight, and the glow flickered against Rusty's open eyes. Rusty's jaw moved as he listened.

"Hey you," Joseph's mother said playfully, after a long pause. "You keep that hand to yourself!" She giggled a little.

*

Joseph woke in the night; he could feel something pressing against him, and when he opened his eyes, the tent's thin walls were almost phosphorescent with moonlight. Rusty's sleeping bag was rolled close to his, and he could feel Rusty's body moving. Inside their sleeping bags, they were like strange, unearthly creatures—thick caterpillars, cocoons. Rusty was rocking against him and whispering, though the words blurred together in a steady rhythm, rising and falling until Joseph could almost make out the words, like something lost in the winds:

"Waiting...I've...when are you...O I am waiting for...and you never..." and the rocking quickened for a moment, and he thought Rusty was crying. But Joseph didn't dare open his eyes. He kept himself very still, breathing slowly, as a sleeper would. Rusty was making a sound, a high thread of tuneless humming, which, after a moment, Joseph realized was the word "Mom," stretched impossibly thin, unraveling and unraveling. And Joseph knew that this was something he could never speak of, to anyone.

Yet even then, even in this still and spooky moment, there was a kind of happiness: something wondrous in Rusty's whispered words, in the urgent pressing of Rusty's body, a secret almost glimpsed. What was it? What was it?

He couldn't ask Rusty, who was more silent and sullen than ever in the week after they returned from their camping trip. He would disappear for hours sometimes, trailing a heavy silence behind him, and if Joseph did encounter him—lying face up in a ditch thick with tall pigweed and sunflowers, or hunkered down by the lumber pile behind the garage—Rusty would give him a look so baleful that Joseph knew he shouldn't approach.

When Rusty had first come to live with them, Joseph said, "Am I supposed to call Rusty my brother?" They were sitting at the supper table, and both his father and mother stopped short and looked up.

"Well," Joseph's father said cautiously. "I know we'd sure like it if Rusty thought of us as his family. But I think it's up to Rusty what you call him." Joseph felt bad at the way that Rusty shrank when they all looked at him. Rusty froze, and his face seemed to pass through a whole series of uncertain expressions.

Then he smiled. "Sure, Joseph," he said. "Let's be brothers." And he showed Joseph a special high-five, where you pressed your thumbs together after slapping palms. You pressed your thumb against the other person's, and each of you fluttered your four fingers. It made the shape of a bird, probably an eagle or a falcon.

It didn't really make them brothers. Joseph knew that Rusty had probably only said something nice to please Joseph's parents, just as he sometimes called them "Uncle Dave," and "Aunt Colleen" to make them happy. But that was OK. *Something* had happened. Something strange and unexplainable passed through the pads of their thumbs when they slid against each other.

This was what Joseph thought of as he watched Rusty. That day, Rusty was slouching thoughtfully near an abandoned house not far from where they lived. Joseph had traced him that far, but he kept his distance. He watched through a pair of his father's binoculars as Rusty picked up an old beer bottle and broke it on a stone, throwing back his arm with a pitcher's flourish. The windows in the old house were already broken out, but Rusty hit at the empty frames with a stick for a while. He lifted his head and looked around, suspiciously. He didn't see Joseph, who was hidden in a patch of high weeds, and after a time, feeling somewhat content, Rusty settled onto his haunches and began to smoke some of the marijuana he'd taken from Joseph's parents' dresser.

Joseph observed: the way his eyes closed as he drew smoke into his mouth, and the way he held it in his lungs, then exhaled in a long breath. For a moment, Rusty let the handmade cigarette hang loosely from his lips, like a movie detective. Then he inhaled again.

Rusty seemed more relaxed when he finally came back to the house, around dinner time. He even deigned to play a game of Super Mario Brothers with Joseph, which he almost never did. They sat side by side on the living room floor, urging Super Mario through obstacles, dodging and jumping, and when Joseph discovered a magic mushroom that would make him invincible for several turns, Rusty gave him the old high-five. He grinned at Joseph kindly. "Rock on," Rusty said.

But that night, as he and Joseph lay in bed, all Rusty wanted to talk about was leaving. New York. Los Angeles. Nashville. Learning how to play electric guitar. He was thinking of writing a letter to the rock band Judas Priest, and asking if he could work for them.

"I'll take you with me," Rusty said. "When we go. Judas Priest is very cool. I could tell them you were my little brother. And we were, like, homeless or something. They'd probably teach us to play instruments. So, you know, when they got older, we would take over. We'd be, like, Judas Priest, Part 2."

"What would I be?" Joseph asked. He wanted to see himself in this new world clearly, to imagine it whole, as Rusty had.

"Probably the drummer," Rusty said. "You like drums, don't you?"

"Yes," Joseph said. He waited, wanting to hear more about himself as a drummer, but Rusty merely folded his hands behind his head.

"We'd probably have to kill them, you know, " Rusty said.

"Who?" Joseph asked. "Judas Priest?"

"No, asshole," Rusty said irritably. "Dave and Colleen. Your parents. I mean, we could get the gun while they were sleeping and it wouldn't even hurt them. It would just be like they were asleep. We could take your dad's car, you know. I could drive."

Joseph thought of his father's new Jeep Rambler, in the driveway, still shiny from its carwash. He pictured sitting in the passenger seat, with Rusty behind the wheel. He didn't say anything for a minute. He didn't know whether Rusty was joking or not, and he was both scared and exhilarated.

He watched as Rusty drew his bare foot out from beneath the covers and picked at a knobby toe. "You could kill the little kids first, while they were sleeping. It wouldn't hurt them, you know. It wouldn't matter. And then, with the gunshots, your mom and dad would come running in, and you could shoot them when they came through the door..." He paused, dreamily, looking at Joseph's face. "And then if you lit the house on fire, no one would ever know what happened. All the evidence, all the bodies and everything would be burned up."

He said this steadily, but his eyes seemed to darken as he spoke, and Joseph felt his neck prickle. He watched as Rusty's mouth hardened, trying to tighten over a quiver of his lips, a waver in his expression. He said, "They'd think we died too. They wouldn't come looking for us, because," he whispered, *"they wouldn't know we were still alive."*

Rusty stared at him, his face lit silver in the moonlight, and Joseph could feel a kind of dull, motionless panic rising inside him, as in a dream. A part of him wanted to shout out for his mother, but he didn't. Instead, he slid his legs slowly onto the tile of the floor. "I have to go to the bathroom," he said, and stood, uncertainly. For a minute, he thought he would start to run.

But the minute he stood up, Rusty moved quickly, catching him by the arm. He caught Joseph and held tightly; he pulled Joseph close to him. The sweet, coppery smell of feet hung on his bare skin, as he pulled Joseph against him.

"Shh!" Rusty's fingers gripped, pinching Joseph's arms. "Don't scream!" Rusty whispered urgently, and Joseph could feel Rusty's muscles tighten. They stood there in a kind of hug, and Rusty pressed his mouth close to Joseph's ear, so that Joseph could feel Rusty's lips brush against the soft lobe. Rusty didn't let Joseph go, but his grip loosened. "Shh," he said. "Don't cry, Joseph. Don't be scared." He had begun to rock back and forth a bit, still holding Joseph, still shushing. "We're like brothers, aren't we? And brothers love each other. Nothing bad's going to happen to you, cause I'm your brother, man, I won't let it. Don't be scared." And Joseph looked up at Rusty's face. He didn't know whether Rusty was telling the truth or not, but he nodded anyway. Rusty's eyes held him as they rocked together, and Joseph swallowed tears and phlegm, closing his mouth tightly. It was true. They did love each other.

For the next few days, or maybe weeks, Rusty paid attention to Joseph. There were times when Joseph thought of that night that Rusty had talked of killing, of lighting fires, and there were even times when he felt that it would probably happen, sooner or later. But when he woke from a bad dream, Rusty was always awake, sitting on the edge of the bed, saying, "It's OK, don't be afraid," passing his hand slowly across Joseph's face, his fingers tracing Joseph's eyelids until they shut. During the day, Joseph and Rusty would take walks, strolling silently out into the bare stubble fields. An occasional jackrabbit would spring up from a patch of weeds and bolt away, leaving little puffs of dust behind its large, fleeing feet. They turned over rocks and found sow bugs, centipedes, metallic-shelled beetles. Sometimes, Rusty found fossils, and he and Joseph took them home and examined them under a magnifying glass. After a while, Joseph's worries passed away; he stopped thinking he should tell his parents about what Rusty had said that night. Rusty himself never spoke of it again. Sometimes, as they looked at the fossils—imprints of fish bones and ferns and clam shells—Rusty would lean over Joseph, letting his face softly brush Joseph's hair. It was said that there had once been a great sea covering the land where they now lived. That was where the fossils came from.

In those days and weeks near the end of the summer, it seemed that something strange was happening to Joseph's family. They were not dead, not burned up, but they seemed to have taken on the qualities of ghosts, without knowing it. There was baby Tom sitting on the sofa, solemnly staring at Joseph, motionless, his mouth very small and stern. There was Cecilia, skipping at the edge of the lilac bush, talking to herself softly in different voices, the sun behind her, making her shadow-like, so it seemed for a moment that she disappeared, melting into the branches and leaves.

Once, at night, he opened his eyes and his mother had been standing over him, in her pale, silky nightgown. A flash of distant lightning made her glow for a moment, and when she reached across him to close the open window above his head, the nightgown rippled and fluttered in a sudden wind, as if she might be lifted up like a piece of ragged cloth.

In the morning, when Joseph came down for breakfast, his mother was kneeling on the kitchen floor, tying the laces of Joseph's father's boots as Joseph's father sat in a chair at the table. They had been talking softly, but they stopped when they saw Joseph standing there.

"Breakfast will be ready in a little bit," she said. Joseph's father's head was drooping, and he didn't look up, only rolled his eyes in Joseph's direction. "Why don't you go outside and play," Joseph's mother said. "I'll call you when breakfast is ready."

One day, not long later, Joseph and Rusty came across his father sitting at the kitchen table, practicing picking up a cup with his prosthetic hand. They watched as he lifted it, set it down, lifted it, set it down, over and over. He was mumbling to the cup, cursing it. "Bitch," his father whispered at the cup, and they were very quiet as the cup wavered in the air, liquid spilling over the trembling cup's edge as his father hardened his eyes, hating the cup. Joseph's father brought the cup to his lips and then it slipped through the metal pinchers and fell to the floor. "Dirty bitch," Joseph's father hissed as the cup broke into shards of porcelain and splashes of coffee. Rusty tugged Joseph's arm, pulling him back. They knew they must not be seen.

There were times, during that last month of summer, when it seemed that he and Rusty were the only ones alive. The rest of Joseph's family seemed to be in a kind of trance, sleepwalkers that he and Rusty moved among. Joseph imagined them jolting awake, suddenly, blinking. "Where are we?" they would say. "What happened to us?"

But the trance didn't break. Instead, the rest of Joseph's family often seemed like statues in a faraway garden, people under a curse, frozen, while Joseph and Rusty walked in the distance.

Across the stubble field, in the old abandoned house, they gathered wood together and made a little bonfire in the center of what must have been the living room. They pretended it was after a nuclear holocaust, and they were the only two people alive. The smoke rose in a sinewy column and crawled along the ceiling toward the broken windows. Joseph and Rusty took vegetables from the garden and put them in a coffee can with water and made a delicious soup, boiled over their fire. Later, they put one of Cecilia's Barbies in the can with a G.I. Joe. They watched as the dolls' plastic limbs melted together, drooping and dripping. Removed from the heat, the two were fused together in a single charred mass.

Kissing: on the floor of the old house, shirtless, Rusty on top of him, their hands clasped, Rusty's sticky skin against his own, their mouths open. When Joseph closed his eyes, it felt as if a small, eager animal was probing the inside of his mouth. It felt funny; he liked it.

It didn't mean he was a fag, Rusty said, and Joseph nodded. There were children at Joseph's school who were called fags. They were too skinny, or too fat; they were weak, or wore stupid clothes, or had funny voices. You knew to avoid them because their loneliness would stick to you.

"You can't tell anybody," Rusty said. "Ever." He traced his finger along Joseph's lips, and then down, along Joseph's neck, his chest, his belly button.

"I know," said Joseph, and when Rusty lowered his body, Joseph let his tongue move over Rusty's chest. *They wouldn't know we were still alive,* Joseph thought, and he closed his eyes. For a moment, it was true: his family was dead, and he and Rusty were on their way together somewhere, and it was all right. He wasn't scared anymore. His lips brushed against Rusty's nipple and he liked the strange, nubby way it felt. He pressed his tongue against it, and was surprised by the way Rusty's body jolted.

Rusty rolled off of him, pushing away, and Joseph's eyes opened. He watched as Rusty knelt in the corner of the old house, unzipping his jeans.

"What are you doing?" Joseph said, and Rusty hunched himself fiercely.

"I'm jerking off, you moron," Rusty said hoarsely. "What, do you want me to fuck you?"

Joseph took a step closer, trying to see what Rusty was doing to his penis, but Rusty gritted his teeth and glared, so he kept his distance.

"Would it hurt?" Joseph said, after a moment, and Rusty hunched even further, the muscles of his back tightening.

"Yes," Rusty hissed. "It would hurt." And he was silent for a moment. "Get out of here, you faggot! Get lost! I mean it!"

And Joseph had slowly backed away, uncertainly. He stood in the high weeds at the door of the house, waiting. There was the summer churr of cicadas; grasshoppers jumped from the high sunflowers and pigweed into his hair, and he shook them off.

"Rusty?" he called. "Rusty?" After a time, he went cautiously back into the house, but Rusty wasn't there. Though Joseph looked everywhere, Rusty didn't appear until supper time.

And then it was over. A week later, they returned to school. They didn't go back to the old house together, and, though they would wait together for the bus in the morning, Rusty was distant. Whatever had happened between them was gone. Why? Joseph thought. Why? But Rusty wouldn't say anything. When Joseph tried to talk to Rusty at night, Rusty would pretend to be asleep. Once, when he tried to get in bed next to Rusty, Rusty kicked him, hard—hard enough to send him across the room with a clatter that brought his mother running.

"Joseph fell out of bed," Rusty said solemnly, and Joseph just sat there on the floor, crying, while his mother stared at them.

"What's going on here?" she said, and Rusty shrugged.

"Nothing," he said, and Joseph crawled back into his own bed, silently.

"Nothing," Joseph said.

Joseph waited for a long time after his mother had left before he spoke. "Rusty," he said. "What did I do? Why don't you like me anymore?"

But Rusty was silent. His breath came out in a threatening sigh.

When Rusty killed himself, a month later, it seemed like a long time had unfolded. Joseph had become used to Rusty's silences. Joseph was involved in school, and the time in the summer had already begun to seem like a long time ago.

He found Rusty in the old living room of the abandoned house. A small bonfire was dwindling, and Rusty's body was splayed out, arms wide, legs spread-eagle, propped in a sitting position against the wall. Rusty had taken one of Joseph's father's guns, put it in his mouth, and pulled the trigger. Later, Joseph learned that it was the anniversary of Rusty's family's death. That was why they said he did it. The bottom half of his face had been blown off, but his eyes were still open. They seemed to have been coated with a thick, smoky film.

Joseph didn't remember leaving the old house. He must have made his way through the weeds, across the stubble field, to the kitchen, where his parents were sitting there, drinking coffee. He could hear the sound of the television. It was Saturday morning, and Cecilia and baby Tom were still watching cartoons.

Years later, Joseph thought there must have been something he missed. Some bit of unremembered time, something that would help him make sense of it all. But it was surprisingly blank. He recalled the moment in the tent, and the night Rusty talked of killing; he recalled the steady effort of his father to hold a cup, to pick up a pen from the bare slick table. He remembered kissing. He remembered waking up in the morning with Rusty pressed against him, holding him tight, feeling Rusty's warm breath against his shoulder blades. But he didn't know what had happened, really. And now he would never know.

He stood at the screen door, and the kitchen seemed to stretch out like a tunnel. It was as if his own life were being separated from him; he would forever float outside it, a ghost hovering above himself. His mother looked at him, her eyes tired and sad. His father raised his prosthetic hand, clicking the hooks together, and then he gave Joseph a wink.

"Hey there, little man," Joseph's father said, as Joseph waved vaguely.

He wanted to tell them, but his throat was dry. "Rusty's dead," he wanted to say, and he watched as they turned to him, smiling: grown suddenly huge in their sweetness, in their lostness, in their gentle, helpless unknowing.

MALACHI BLACK

To One Waiting to Be Born

1.

Know your origin: you are a token
of the afterwards of love. What flinches
in the ribbon of your utterly new blood
is nothing but the echo of a bed post—
pulse.
        You have grown up. From filament
within your mother's bulb, you have evolved
into a chandelier of bones, weightlessly
orbiting your portion of the womb, aglow
in skin that holds you as an astronaut's
upholstery. Small ghost, your figure
is almost your own. You fidget, but
be still. Be whole. Rotate like a globe
until, too old, you can't be steadfasted
by axes. Your center has already lost
its poles.

2.

        Soon you will be divulged.
Good luck: you won't be born as much
as you'll be given up. And as you tumble
from your orbit toward this crib of sticks
and dust, be adamant. Be tough. All earth
is but a roughness underfoot. To be delivered
is too little and too much: it is the touch
that will disfigure you that you must learn
to touch. You will scuff and stain and ruin
like a patent leather boot, and stagger
haplessly through weather that gnarls
what is new. Your first face will be forgotten

as a field is under snow, and you will
let yourself be vandalized as all handsomeness
will. There is no balm for what is rotten,
and you will spoil like a plum, but still
wash every day and wash again the rancid
blemish that your body has become.

                     Stare into your hands.
How can you doubt that you are animal?

3.

This is your ontology: you are
because you must be someone's child.
Be otherwise. Be wild: be stranger
and more formless than a boy.
                              Cast off
the membrane that has covered you,
unwind the muscle that encumbers
you, and rise:
                    twirl as a whirlwind
overhead, effortlessly aerial,
incorporeal, almost electrical—
drift as a bright curl in the bluish light
of sky: impervious, indifferent, unhuman.

MALACHI BLACK
When I Lie Down

to Sleep

I'll count backward from a thousand
till my teeth begin to grind, down

to zero, where the digits tilt and swivel
in a ring around the racing eye

of the tornado I'm made of tonight.
Left alive, I am an opening

too wide, much too much gaping sky
to slip behind the throbbing canopy

of hide I call an eyelid. So let your crow
land in my lashes; close my eyes.

I'll be your nest, a place to rest
built out of syllables of lullabies:

Come to me. Don't go. We have nothing left
to say to one another but hello.

MALACHI BLACK

Prayer for a Slow Death

Let the light be
yellow but not   candle-lit, quiet,
                        incandescent,   not cold yet
                                                  not quite bright

enough to sting
the eye, close   enough to see
                        beside, clear   enough to read
                                                 by, and just near

enough to turn
off morning   after morning,
                        to burn on   absentmindedly
                                                 each night

KIM CHINQUEE
The Meat Place

I'm driving my aunt Sarah's Lexus, taking us to the meat place. We pass farms with pastures full of Holsteins and green trees. Weeds fill the ditches. Beyond, in the woods, are deer, raccoons, and skunks. Sometimes, driving on the road, I see them try to cross. Sometimes I see a carcass.

I used to see these fields, living on a farm nearby. Then my parents divorced and I moved to town with my mother. I was fifteen and it was a hard time for me. When we'd drive back to the old place, I'd look out at the fields, my body feeling like a graveyard, hardly thinking what was out there.

That's when my aunt and I got close. She lived in town, and would ask me to come over, paying me to vacuum. I'd clean the toilets, scrub the mirrors, and dust. Sometimes she gave me money to go shopping, saying to get my uncle Harry white cotton shirts in extra-larges, and for her, a sweatshirt. I'd always give her the receipts, and she'd hand me a ten or twenty that I might put away for later. I'd use some of it for lunch. My mom had filed for assistance, so at school I was supposed to get free meals, but I was too embarrassed and never used the tickets.

I still feel the weight of the memory of that time. I stay in the slow lane, letting cars pass, and I try to focus on the highway. Most of the cars are domestic because that's what most of us drive here in the great Midwest. Semis whiz by like storms. Then one semi crosses over to my lane. I try to press the horn. I hear nothing, so I scream. I jerk onto the shoulder.

My aunt holds onto the door. She points and says, "The horn's there in the middle."

She says, "It's only fifty-five here, but I go a little faster."

We are just outside the city, almost to the place where local farmers and hunters take their poultry, veal, and beef. Before Harry got sick, he'd kill his deer, butcher them, and skin them. He'd bring whatever was left to the meat place.

When I was a kid, my family hired a butcher to slaughter our own cows, ones too old for milking. It's just how we did things. Then when I turned eight, I was put in charge of wrapping. I remember the feel of the warm meat, wrapping it with paper, sealing it with tape and labeling whatever part I was told it was with the fat black pen that smelled like glue and copper. Sirloin, ground round, cube steak, tail and heart and tongue. After I was done, I'd put them in a giant cooler. My mom kept track of things on a pad of yellow paper.

She'd talk to the butcher, saying things like "Sorry my daughter's so slow. She's a little Cinderella."

My mother would tell me to speed up. Hearing that would send me trying to wrap faster, but then I'd forget what I just wrapped, having to unwrap again so I'd label it correctly. That only frustrated her more, and she'd say things to me like "Your father will be mad. We'll be late for supper."

My dad was always off doing all his own stuff: plowing, planting corn, maybe cleaning stanchions or helping a cow with a delivery, wrapping a rope around a newborn's slimy hooves once the calf started to emerge. He'd use most of his strength to try to pull. If the calf was born a bull, he never kept it. He only kept the heifers, since they'd eventually be milking, and that's where my father made his profit. He hired breeders from a place called Midwest Breeders.

My dad ordered semen from a catalog, and he would lock the in-heat cow into a stanchion. Then the breeder arrived, bringing his boots, his apron, his long-sleeved gloves, his case. I wasn't allowed to watch the rest. My dad would say, "Go away. You don't need to see this."

The breeder was always the same guy. I called him Mister Gene. We belonged to the same church and his son James was in my class. He was the first boy I had a crush on—we'd send each other notes under our desks, saying things like "I really like you." He left me squares of Bubble Yum, and we held hands once on the bus.

When James came along with his father, I'd hope to see him, going out and doing chores like feeding the calves an extra bale of hay or combing one with the brush to get her ready for the fair. James was in 4-H like me, and we both showed cows and heifers.

At home in the basement, my family had two gigantic freezers, with all different kinds of meat and organs—I thought this kind of thing was common until I started talking about it with my friends as an adult. I never questioned it until my friends seemed alarmed to hear I ate my favorite cow, Iona. I loved that cow. When I fed her weeds under the fence, she always let me pet her.

Now in the car, my aunt says, "Look, a buck," pointing to the woods. I see her hands, all veined and thin. Since her cancer diagnosis months before, her psyche has gone shaky.

"Where?" I say.

"Over there," she says. "Maybe we should get Harry some venison or sausage."

I say, "He wanted the ground round."

I've been cooking nonstop for my aunt and uncle. I flew in last week from New York. I haven't been here in two years. I don't like coming back, but they're in bad shape and I feel as though I have to do something.

I try to cook low-fat, since Harry's heart thing and then his complications. Two months after his attack, he went in for surgery to have a stent replaced, only to be rushed back that night to the ER when he couldn't stop throwing up and bleeding. One, two, three, all those days, I'd call him on his cell phone from New York, hearing beeping, the alarm of an IV, a lab tech in to draw his blood work. I could hear him chattering in the background, saying, "Another stick?" then "No, it doesn't hurt much."

"I hope you're in good hands," I'd say.

When I'd say, "Where is Aunt Sarah?" he'd say, "Oh, she's back at home. She hasn't been so well. She won't tell me much. Yesterday, Shirley stopped over and found her passed out in the hallway."

Shirley is their friend. She's stressed from keeping track of them. The day before I came, she called and said, "I can't be there all the time." She sounded impatient.

I said, "You don't have to be. Why should you?"

She said, "I have to take care of my own life."

Now my aunt hardly eats, is sometimes curled over saying, "Fuck," there's a hiccup in her backbone, her stomach an explosion. She says, "Fuck the pain. This fucking pain!"

And then she'll take some pills: the Oxy or the Lexapro or Xanax, or the estrogen blocker with the complicated name that's supposed to stop the spreading of her cancer. She shouldn't be drinking. She was a drinker before her cancer, but after her diagnosis, she started drinking daily. Since I got here, she's snuck out twice to get her pints of vodka, slamming as much as she could before making it home again.

The last time, after she woke, as she staggered and fell into the wall, I asked, "Are you hung over?" She leaned and asked me, "How'd you know?"

She's only sixty-five and she shouldn't be this sick yet.

She's the same age as Harry and my mom. They all went to high school together.

My mom is somewhere with a new guy on vacation and isn't here to help. My dad's been dead two years. It was a suicide, part of his mental illness, even though he was living in a place where people came three times a day to check on him and give him medication. One day, a social worker found him hanging in the bedroom. I heard about it from my aunt. She'd left a message on my voicemail, saying, "Please call me. It's important."

We pass a store where my dad used to get things for his farm: welding hats and shovels, nails, and tools to burn off horns of heifers. I remember going with him. Though I'm not sure why, my mother said I had to. I'd ride shotgun in his truck, looking out the window, holding my lips shut, afraid something would set off my dad and he'd start yelling. When he got to the lot, I followed him in. As he paced the aisles, I tried to lag behind him. He never said what he was doing. The building had high ceilings and a cement floor, and things were stacked in crates and boxes. It smelled like manure and rust.

Passing by the store, I say to my aunt, "That's where my dad used to get his farm stuff."

I want to ask her what it was like to grow up with my dad, if he played with trains, or if he had a thing for swing sets. People say my baby pictures look like his. As a boy, he had big eyes and long lashes. Some pictures show him in his barn clothes. The older he gets, the more his face gets stoic. Looking through the albums, I never find the mean face I was scared of. He was fit and handsome, like people on TV. He had thick blond hair with a cowlick above the left side of his forehead.

I keep trying to ask my aunt things about her life as a child, what my dad was like, if there were signs and problems. When I first got here again this time, when I asked those things, she said, "I don't remember." She got up and said, "How 'bout some wine?" She poured and poured. She slipped me hundred-dollar bills, and I wanted to ask again about my dad, but I knew by then she'd probably forgotten.

"Are you OK?" I say to my aunt as we near the meat place. She looks a little restless.

She says to me, "Pull up," pointing to a gas station called Grand Central.

I prepare to sit and wait. I watch her clutch her purse and open the door. People go in and out in Packer shirts and John Deere hats, but there are also men in ties, women wearing blazers. I turn on the air. A man leans on his Ford, bouncing a toddler in diapers. His thick hair and pretty smile remind me of my boyfriend, Brad, who calls me every day when he's walking my Chihuahua.

My aunt might be a while, so I call Brad. After our hellos, I ask him, "Did you run?"

He says to me, "Not yet."

I picture his green eyes. It was the first thing I noticed when we met for a run around the park next to the zoo, where you can see the giraffes' necks if you look in the right places. That day, I heard an elephant, a roar. We ran that loop three times, talking about hill repeats and getting shoes stuck in the mud when running trails and competing in cross-country.

He says, "Are you OK?"

I say to him, "I think I am. I will be."

He says, "I know it's hard."

I say, "It's probably good I came."

He's been listening to me struggle. When I first heard about the return of my aunt's cancer, I cried on his bare skin, and he just stayed there and he held me.

We went to the zoo, where we held hands, and looked at the giraffes. We bought peanuts and fed them to the elephants, watching them move their trunks like Slinkys. We watched the monkeys swing, and heard their sounds like coughing. My eyes felt red, and my insides felt like a soppy rag that was getting a good cleansing.

Still, I don't expect Brad to know what it's like for me to be here. I like his mom, his dad, his sister and her kids. They have me over and ask me how I am. They set a plate for me, and ask if I want seconds. They offer me dessert. They say there is no pressure.

I look at the dash and see a blinking light. It's circular and red. I say, "It's good I'm here."

He says, "I really miss you."

I say, "I miss you too," looking at the console. I think my aunt's been inside for a while, though I'm not sure how long.

"Sugarplum," he says. "I have to go to work now."

After we hang up, I push a button, trying to find music. I find a station where a woman's voice is singing about rainbows. It reminds me of my mother humming to the radio on our way to church as my father drove his Silverado. The one time I leaned ahead and asked to change the channel, my mother said, "Stay quiet with your lips tight. You'll make your father happy."

She started saying that a lot. It took me a while to realize that meant my father didn't want to be bothered. After that I started to bite my lips so hard it seemed they were always bleeding.

I'm thirsty, so when I see my aunt's bottled water in the holder, I reach for it and sip. This one is water. This morning, I gave her a water bottle filled with vodka.

The first couple days, I tried to stop her. Each morning I was there, she'd pace and fidget with her keys, saying she had to run an errand, get things like mineral water, chocolate milk, or coffee. She'd leave just before eight, the time places in Wisconsin can start selling liquor.

Sometimes she'd leave earlier, but she wouldn't come back till sometime after eight. One time, she left around six, said she had to get lettuce from the grocer, and after she left, my uncle said, "She sometimes drinks vanilla extract."

She'd come home and then pass out until it was time for more. I tried to understand her pain. I was pretty sure she'd die soon.

Then Harry took her keys. I wasn't sure what to do then, but I decided I couldn't stop her. She's hurting and she's scared. This is all she has now. So last night, I bought a pint of vodka and a large bottle of water. I drank that water, slamming the whole thing, remembering how water is supposed to flush you. I poured the vodka in the bottle. I got up three times that night and peed. After I woke at 6 a.m., I sat in the living room with the vodka. When she came around, pacing, up the stairs, then down, she asked me where her keys were. I said, "Harry doesn't want you driving."

Her shoulders drooped, and it seemed the rest of her just followed. She nodded and she said to me, "OK."

I sat there for a while. I heard and watched her pace. When I sensed her in the kitchen, I got up and went there and I handed her the bottle. I said, "It isn't water."

As she took a sip, her eyes glowed. "Whoa!" she said. "I thought that was water."

I said to her, "I'm sorry. I don't know what to do." I felt a little sick.

She hugged me and she said, "That's OK." She hugged me again and she said, "Thank you."

Now when she comes out of the gas station, I can't tell if she looks any different. When she gets in the car, I say, "Did you get rid of the evidence?"

She says, "How'd you know?"

I was there when Harry found the empty half-pint in her purse. He showed it to her. He asked her, "What is this?" and after she sat up and staggered to the bathroom, he said to me, "How can we ever stop her?"

I said, "We can't. She's frightened and in pain. It's the only thing that helps her."

He said, "But she says she wants to stop. I've told her that I've had it. I can't be with her when she's like this."

Now she hugs her purse and says, "I only drank half of it."

As I drive across the lot to the meat place, I say, "Do you want me to go in?"

She opens her door and says, "Yes, let's," and on the way in, she hands me a bunch of crumpled hundreds. I see her heading to the bathroom, taking small, quick steps that remind me of my grandma. My aunt wears a cap to cover her bald spots. Her pants are the same from days before: baggy, matching the oversize university sweatshirt from the supply she gets from the outlet.

I look through the glass cases that seem endless: rows of steaks and pork and chicken. It turns my gut to be here. Venison and sausages and cheese. I take a number from the machine. My number's fifty-four. A man from behind the counter wearing white calls out number fifty. Other customers look through glass like I do. I can tolerate the cooking of the meat, but I can't eat it. I hate seeing the slabs behind the case. It's as if they're lost pieces to a puzzle.

I want to leave. I walk up and down, waiting for my number. I focus on a blond girl wearing pink who puts her tongue on the case until a fat man lifts her. I see bacon, ham. The place smells like jam and mud. I finally hear a fifty-four, and I point to the lean ground round.

On the way home, we drive through roundabouts. They are new, with construction cones like carrots. My aunt looks calm. She turns the radio up. "Thank you," she says. I like this car, with its fancy button. You just press it and it starts as long as the keys are in it. The doors won't lock with the keys in it. It's Krupp-proof, my aunt told me. She and I, we're Krupps. We make crumbs and are forgetful. We lose things. We can't find our direction.

Nearing the city again, we come up to the stoplight where, at fifteen, I got hit. I was on my bike. It was sprinkling, dark. I was wearing a white sweater and baggy pinstriped pants. I remember lying on the pavement. Staring at the sky. I remember being peaceful.

My aunt says, "Do you think anything is up there?"

I say, "I don't know. I hope."

She says, "Besides sky?"

I say, "I believe everyone is something. Responsibility, integrity, compassion. I know it. I believe."

She says, "My dad was such a bastard. I hated how he preached at us. I got tired of his god talk."

I say, "He used to make me feel important, paying so much attention to me."

She says to me, "You *are* important."

I say, "I used to think I loved him."

I've told her this story before. After my parents divorced, since my father was so sick and suicidal, there was no question I'd be living with my mother. Then one day after school, my grandfather came over with my grandma. I was there alone; my dad was in the barn and my mother was getting things set up in the new place. My grandpa said, "You should be living with your father."

I was scared of my father. I knew I didn't want to live with him.

My grandpa said, "He needs you."

I just stood there looking up at his eyes behind his glasses.

He said, "Don't you know what's right?"

He wore a crisp white shirt. He smelled of cinnamon, molasses. My grandmother stood next to him, wearing polyester.

I said, "I'm not sure I can stay here."

He said, "Your father needs you."

I said, "I'm scared. I'm sorry."

He seemed to appear taller. He pointed, saying, "You're a sinner. You'll be damned." Then I watched him take my grandma's hand, head out the door, and back out of the driveway.

I hear sirens, so I pull off to the side. An ambulance speeds by.

Back on the road I say, "I don't want you to suffer. Tell me what to do."

My hands sweat at the wheel. She says, "I just want you here. I think you understand. You're so unlike Shirley. She acts like my mother."

I remember calls to Shirley weeks before I came. She went on and on about the things my aunt was doing. I say, "Shirley doesn't know what to do. She cares for you. She's scared."

My aunt says, "So am I. I'm not sure I trust my doctor."

The wheel is sticky. The car floats away from me. I brake so hard my neck hurts.

I say to her, "Why not?"

"He's lying. I can feel it."

"Why would he lie?"

"He doesn't do anything to help."

I say, "Don't skip any more appointments. Tell him you need more for the pain. Maybe you should be telling things like this to Harry."

"He just wants to interfere."

"He wants to be a part. You have to let him in. He's taking it personally."

When I'd call, he'd tell me she'd been at it. When she'd come to the phone, she'd mumble things that sounded like snow on a TV screen. I couldn't understand her. She might say, "I don't think they know what they're doing."

I'd call Shirley, who'd already tried to call the doc, the social worker, even the cops and legal people. Once, she rang the doorbell and found my aunt dead-looking on the sofa. She woke my uncle. He tried to carry her. Shirley called 911. My aunt ended up in the ICU with an alcohol level hardly anyone had heard of.

But a time or two, she'd talk clearly and tell me of her treatment, about the estrogen blockers that were supposed to stop the spreading of her cancer. Once, she said, "I hate them."

I say, "Talk to Harry. It would help him if he knew that."

A week before I flew out, Harry called and said, "She drove into the mailbox. So I took her keys, and the next night, she walked a mile to Grand Central. I didn't get a call from her until 8 a.m. The cops found her in the ditch and she was in the psych ward." I still imagine her up on the ninth floor, in the same psych ward where my dad went.

In another conversation, when Harry talked about his first attack, he said, "I touched my heart and fell. Everything went black and then the pain left. I woke when Sarah touched me." I was on my end of the phone, sitting at my desk. I closed my eyes. I wanted to reach out. He didn't seem old before that.

We're almost home. My aunt Sarah nods herself to sleep. We pass the high school I attended, where I ran track and cross-country and cheered for the wrestlers. I'd walk to class each morning, late, having to stop at the office to pick up my detentions, my stomach growling, telling myself I can wait for lunch, where I would allow myself an apple or a handful of peanuts.

My aunt wakes, saying, "Did we get the meat?"

"Yes," I say, and then she giggles.

As we pass another gas station, she points and says, "Let's stop there." It's the same place where—when I was in high school—my friends and I would find some man outside to take our cash and get us Old Style, PBR, whatever was the cheapest.

I know she craves more alcohol, but I'm afraid she might pass out on me. I say, "We better not." I hear a ring. It confuses me, another fancy feature on this car. I push the phone tab on the dashboard.

"Hello?" I realize it's my uncle.

He asks me, "Are you with her?"

I say, "You were sleeping when we left. We didn't want to disturb you."

"But is she OK?"

I look at her. Back to the phone I say, "She's OK. We got your meat. The lean stuff."

He says, "I like it fresh and raw."

I tell him, "I remember."

I look at my aunt again, her head against the window. I turn back to the phone. "You holding up?" I say.

He says, "I'm about to mow the lawn."

I imagine him falling. Blades. "That's not a good idea," I say. "Let me." I like to mow the lawn—it was my job when I was on the farm, and I'd ride all day on the tractor, up the hills and down them, going fast around the trees, speeding up as I was edging closer.

"I'll go slow," he says. "I need to do something."

As I turn onto the street, I nudge my aunt, say, "Sarah."

She turns to me, says, "Hey!" She laughs. She giggles. She mumbles something about Mars and she asks me if we're there yet.

At the house, my uncle sits on a lawn chair in the driveway, wearing shorts and some university T-shirt. He's sweating. I wave to him and pull into the garage, and say to my aunt, "We're here now."

She holds onto the car and walks around it. I grab her arm and help her up the stairs. When I say, "Are you OK?" she gives me the same unexpected smile that I saw in my dad the day before his first breakdown.

I tell Harry, "I'll be back," and I take my aunt to her chair, brown and thick with cushion. She sits and pulls the handle so the footrest comes up. She grabs my hand, says, "Thanks for understanding."

I say to her, "Sit tight," and I go out and find my uncle by the fence with a weed-whacker. He looks fatigued. His arms don't swing with the verve they did when he played all those years of baseball. Golf too. He was into those things before his knees went. He used to be muscular and strong, a hunter. He shot a bear, but didn't kill it. He finally got the moose he wanted. He has the antlers. Also trophies, now in boxes in the basement—he won tournaments in rugby. He served in Vietnam. After leaving the war, he started his own business. He works as an accountant.

A lot of their clients were small business owners who thrived on winning seasons of the Packers. He's blocks from the stadium. He and my aunt have season tickets, and once I went to a game with my aunt and Shirley. It was so much different from when I used to go in high school. Back then, my friend Jan and I used to sit outside the stadium waiting for anyone to scalp us tickets. I was always cold, wearing shoes not meant for socks. We'd be in the stands and she'd point to this Packer player and then that one. I wasn't sure how all that worked but she'd tell me that she fucked them. When I went with my aunt and Shirley, we wore layers of green and walked there. We lifted ourselves and did the wave hardcore.

At the office, my aunt and uncle stocked the break room with stuff like fruit snacks and Little Debbies. Sausages and cheese. Mineral water and any kind of soda. My mom never had much food. We didn't have a lot of money. She wasn't around much, and when she was, she'd be with a different man, laughing in her room in the basement.

The office got really busy during tax time. My uncle would spend all his time there. He had his attack there. He was at his desk, two days before the IRS deadline.

Now I sit on the step and watch him working through a row. The lawn isn't thick. I mowed it the day after I got here and so far, it's been a dry summer.

"You holding up?" I say. I'm tired from the effort. Since arriving, I've also been cleaning. Laundry and the dishes. Cooking and watering the plants. Hosing down the lawn, the trees, the flowers in the garden. Sorting through the mail and collecting calls from tenants living in my aunt and uncle's rentals.

He stays upright, walking to his lawn chair. "I feel great," he says. "I haven't moved in ages."

A truck turns into the driveway. "Hey, Hank," says my uncle, and as the man steps out, I remember him, a ranger at the Wildlife Sanctuary. He wears a camouflage hat, jeans, a shirt that says, "I'm for it."

"Hank," I say.

"Hey," he says. He turns his whole body toward my uncle. He says, "Our oldest skunk died this morning. I'm gonna miss that guy. He was six years old. I really learned to love him."

Harry puts his hand on his friend's shoulder and says, "Hank, remember you're a ranger."

I've been to the sanctuary before, seeing skunks, raccoons, and badgers. I went there on my own the day after my dad died. It comforted me. I remember, as a girl, talking to the cows and cats. I always thought they liked me.

I say, "Do you have any new ones? Animals, I mean?" I really miss my dog now. At home, when I sleep, she burrows under, trying to get close, getting up and barking when she senses her need to protect me.

Hank says, "Today a badger had two pups. And a beaver had a kitten." He talks about the patterns of an owl, how the fledglings copy their parents. He talks of ostriches and chicks. He says, "So Harry? When will we be hunting? I put up new stands on your land so we can study deer tracks."

Harry says, "Maybe in the fall. I'll be like new in no time."

I go inside, where my aunt lies back with her eyes closed. It's past 10 a.m. I go to the guest room, where my things are, by the bed, though most nights I never get there, just like home. I fall asleep to the TV. I like to hear the voices.

I find my shoes, put on a running bra and shorts. I'm grateful for my iPod, a gift from my boyfriend, who tells me I deserve things.

My aunt is still passed out. Back outside, my uncle talks to Hank.

"I'm going to run," I say.

Harry says, "As far as yesterday? And the day before?"

"I'm not sure," I say. "But you don't have to time me."

He laughs a little. Hank waves and I'm not sure what he says because I'm already up on volume.

I step down the street, deciding today I will go right, then left, then right again, passing the first place I moved to after my mother left my dad. Since then, I haven't seen it. I run fast and out of breath, imagining how horrible it felt there. I still can envision when my mom said, "I don't need him," in the car, and how I cried there, looking up at patterns in the ceiling. Everything whirled around. My parents never argued. I realized they didn't talk much.

I turn back and look at that old place, never knowing what I felt then. I run by the church lot where I had sex with my first boyfriend, where he first told me that he loved me. I remember hearing about James, the boy I liked when I was younger. He was the smartest in the class and I was second. Then in high school, after I moved, I learned from an old friend he shot himself in a closet in his bedroom. He used his father's shotgun. I remember crying, wondering, sprinting laps around the track. I wished I'd saved his notes. I never really knew him.

I run a half-mile to that old track. I pull on the gate, but it's locked. I think of climbing over.

I run by the place where I got hit, remembering the accident, that big old sky, then when I saw my bike in shambles.

Farther out, there are dunes where I used to party with my friends in high school. We'd light a fire and sit on logs and pour keg beer into our cups, staying there until the cops came. My mom was never around. She had meetings and appointments. I remember running as a teen, how it always seemed to save me. I think about my aunt. I don't want her to go.

I see the fields. I run faster, going past them. The music is not new. I see green trees and grass and weeds. I go up a hill. I pump my arms and push my body to the top of it.

JAE CHOI
Morning Song I

Greet the walker, walking
in with the shadow of the hood

shooing away the emphatic light.
First cold night the blinds

flicker down, each vinyl strip
a white notion near as wide.

August, gone, feels gone.
The woman in another room,

ever without honeymoon,
hits snooze and spreads her hair

behind her like the patch
of hillside shade I've come to expect

to be disrupted by. The walker's
will to move is too exact for speech.

I boil the milk to pitch, but
couldn't close the door on intractable fire

if you asked me to. A mother on the phone,
receiver lifted to ear, dripping like a red

peony out of water. Each of me, asking
one foot over the chalked line, can I be

walker too? Each of me, peeling
duct tape from the long moan,

crawling under the car to escape
the desert air and the general lack of shadow.

I am on public land, independent
of tree or fear, eating bread that's burned

in the setting sun until the final scene comes
to crush my caked hand with a mean

boot heel stare and you can hear it
hit the audience when they see

that this girl, a woman if I ever
knew one, isn't going anywhere.

JAE CHOI
Fell

A blackish hue
clustered at our heels.

You were in the mixed woods
which meant I was in the same mixed woods.

I kicked up the floor. Needles
littered the lower air in standing dust,

our shadows dotting the dirt mound
sloped unnecessarily away.

I peeled back
in drying nut husks,

upturned trunks of living trees,
massive, deeply split.

A bird trilled
in its straw nest of tips and ends.

Below it, our bodies chambered
the wet bulk, the bank held to bedrock.

What could not be brought inside,
we put to stream-bottom,

we couldn't believe the swarm
could form without our knowing.

But we listened. The apical pulse,
a steady beat above the splinter.

Didn't I say I bled at my burial?
You should have too.

Our bodies in the air,
in a forest, falling,

the forest itself hemmed in
by an abusive logic,

black recess of sap and sticking
shadow. We fell,

all around us small things
kicked up from the undergrowth.

STEPHEN DAU
Nature Walk

an excerpt from In a Foreign Country

The map haunts you. You spotted it the day you arrived, hanging on the back of an office door. The words "Land Mine Areas, Bosnia-Herzegovina" are printed in large letters across the top, and each land mine area is labeled on it with a tiny, pale red dot. When you look at the map from across the room, thirty feet away, you can make out Bosnia's entire road system, as though traced in pink highlighter by an eager toddler.

You think of the map almost every day. You think about it on your way to and from work. You think about it when you walk past the small park off Marsala Titova Street. You think about it when you look up at the hills surrounding the city. You walk only on cement, stand only on asphalt. You regard any grassy or forested areas with suspicion.

Then one day, your boss, Elisabeth, decides to take the staff on a picnic. She has heard that you have brought your guitar with you from America, and she suggests you bring it along. But you see instantly that her vision of the afternoon—a group of joyous Bosnians singing folk songs accompanied by your skillful playing—differs so dramatically from reality—you know nothing more than two R.E.M. songs and the opening riffs of "Purple Haze"—that you hastily decline.

It takes two cars to drive all the staff up into the hills, to a wooded spot close to the ski jump from the 1984 Winter Olympics. You keep forgetting that Sarajevo is a ski town. The steep, pine forest would be gorgeous except for two things: its selection as the picnic site was preceded by a lengthy discussion of whether or not any land mines remain in the area, a discussion that seems not to have been entirely concluded by the time you arrive; and, the amount of trash strewn in the woods makes it look and smell less like a picnic spot and more like a garbage heap.

The cars are parked alongside the road, and everyone gets out and begins reluctantly unloading boxes from the trunks, as though they are humoring the Americans and their strange customs.

"This side is clear," says someone. "The south side is still mined."

"I don't think so," says someone else. "You've got it backwards."

Then suddenly they are walking off into the woods, all of them, one by one, in a line, like lemmings, you think. You pause next to the car. You have heard that the most heavily mined areas usually lie immediately beside the road. You convince yourself that your fellow picnickers have now passed through what would be the most heavily mined area, were this road mined, but as you have no experience with the procedures and techniques used in laying mines, you're not sure. Maybe you are overthinking things. Perhaps you fear obliteration too much. You reluctantly follow, trying to step precisely in the path of bent grass left by the others.

They have found a patch of ground relatively free of debris, and you all sit down to eat the picnic food, which consists of cold, pregrilled *chivapchi* with pita bread and potato salad and cans of cola. After it has been eaten, Elisabeth insists that all the group's garbage be packed up and taken away, a request that prompts the Bosnian members of the staff to shrug their shoulders and grudgingly stuff their trash into plastic bags, which are then loaded into the trunk of one of the cars before being driven back into town.

The apartment in which you live is five rooms in a four-story neoclassical stone building on Marsala Titova Street. It is rented by your employer from an elderly woman who reminds you of your grandmother, who has decorated it the way your grandmother would have decorated an apartment, had your grandmother lived in Eastern Europe, except that there is also a flak jacket in the closet and shrapnel pocks on the walls.

The tiny bedroom has a window that overlooks an inner courtyard. A large flock of pigeons perches on the roof and on the railings directly outside the bedroom window, cooing incessantly. Books left by the apartment's previous occupants fill a shelf on one wall. They include two histories of the Balkans: *Black Lamb and Grey Falcon* by Rebecca West and Noel Malcolm's *A Short History of Bosnia*. Also, the first two volumes of Robert Jordan's *The Wheel of Time* series. *A Farewell to Arms*. An English-Bosnian dictionary and language study book. *The Bridge on the Drina* by Ivo Andrić. *The Three-Arched Bridge* by Ismail Kadare. A short-story collection whose name you will never remember, but which is described in the jacket copy as containing "ten tales

' that shimmer." A Grisham novel. A copy of the Bible. A copy of the Koran. The Robin Buss translation of *The Count of Monte Cristo. The Tibetan Book of Living and Dying* by Sogyal Rinpoche.

An old cabinet-style stereo takes up most of one wall in the dining room. It doesn't work, but a newer portable radio and CD player on top of it does. The radio is tuned to the Armed Forces Network, which broadcasts National Public Radio in the evenings. In the bedroom, a tiny portable television receives three channels, two of which seem to air nothing but Bosnian folk music heavy with accordion, vibrato, and occasional ululation, sung by heavily made-up singers wearing black. The third channel carries infomercials. In the media cabinet under the television is a videocassette of *Noddy,* the British children's television program, and *Absolutely Fabulous,* the British adult television program.

The cast iron tub in the bathroom is enclosed by a makeshift curtain tacked to one wall. The electric water heater mounted on the wall beside it must be turned off at night and turned on each morning, provided there is electricity, because if it is left on overnight and the electricity goes out, the fuse blows and the owner must be called to replace it.

The kitchen contains a gas stove, which usually works, a stainless-steel sink, and an old enameled refrigerator. A door off the kitchen opens onto a small terrace, which you will never use, overlooking the tiny courtyard. The building's residents have taken to dumping their trash into the courtyard, and it is filled with a thick layer of debris: newspapers and empty plastic bottles and beer cans and scraps of food and diapers and old T-shirts and a tennis shoe and Styrofoam packaging and garbage bags blown up like balloons from the gases of whatever is decomposing inside them.

Every so often, one of the many pigeons will spot something, too shiny or edible to resist, lying on the ground in the courtyard, and will fly down to investigate, whereupon a large orange tomcat will launch itself from a shadowed corner in a spray of blood and feathers. You hear the sound of it often, when cooking in the kitchen, or when lying on the bed reading. It sounds like a feathered shuttlecock being whacked with a tennis racket. Eventually, you become so accustomed to the sound that you don't even look up from whatever you are doing, but merely think passingly to yourself, "There goes another one."

*

Your life settles into a sort of nervous, anxiety-ridden routine. Each morning, you wake up and have a shower if there is electricity for hot water and don't if there is not. You walk to work if the weather is nice or take the tram if it's raining. Sometimes you manage to get breakfast along the way, and sometimes you do not. You arrive at the building and go into the office, which is down the hall from a large Siemens branch. You try to arrive every morning before Elisabeth does. You sit at your desk.

Each morning, you read the bulletin, which is cobbled together by the US embassy from various news sources and sent around to all the American NGOs. In it, you read that packs of wild dogs have been spotted roaming the city, and you are cautioned against feeding or otherwise interacting with them. You read that shots were fired and a grenade exploded the previous evening along the Skenderija, and that the police confiscated two Kalashnikovs and several hand grenades. The incident is described as a domestic dispute. You are urged to vary your daily routine, to take different routes between home and work, to avoid political demonstrations or crowds, to remain unpredictable.

You try to familiarize yourself with your work. That work involves introducing the people of the region to Democracy and Capitalism, the combination of which represents, it is universally agreed, the only possible path forward out of ethnic strife and general backwardness. Your job is to select people from Bosnia to send to America to learn how to found banks or generate electricity or treat drinking water or manage accounting firms, or at least learn how these things are done in America. It is thought that this activity will contribute to the development of the communism-scarred and violence-plagued landscape. This is the grand project in which the International Community is engaged, and it is talked about with great enthusiasm. Generally speaking, your job in America was to find the places where these people could learn these things, and now that you are in Bosnia, your job is to find the people who will go and learn them.

You sit at your desk and read about the organizations and people you are there to help. But you have trouble keeping them all straight, while the staff you are supposed to oversee is entirely familiar with them, in the same way any politically engaged American knows who the mayor or governor is, and in the same way any visiting foreign exchange student would not. Occasionally, one of the Bosnian staff members approaches you and tells you what she is working on. She asks you for guidance, and you read over whatever piece of paper or folder she has presented to you and nod thoughtfully. Then you ask her what she thinks she should do, and after she tells you, you tell her to do whatever it is she has just suggested. It's a pantomime, of sorts, played out daily because both participants in the conversation are too polite to do otherwise.

At noon you go to lunch, which is usually chivapchi and pita bread and a can of cola. You eat it outside at a park bench if the weather is nice, or at a plastic table under an awning if it's raining. Then you go back to the office and sit at your desk.

Throughout the day, the nervous, jittery feeling you have felt since the moment you arrived does not go away. It never goes away. Sometimes it is slightly more severe, and sometimes less so, but it is always there. Much of the time you spend sitting at your desk each day is spent wondering what's wrong with you.

When it's time to go home, you take the tram if it's raining or walk if it's not, back down Marsala Titova Street to your apartment. Then you go inside, sit down on the bed, and try to force your hands to stop shaking. You close your eyes. You breathe deeply, but you can't force your heart to stop racing, or the nervous, sickly feeling in your stomach to subside.

In the evenings, you try to occupy yourself. You practice playing your guitar, which you find eases the trembling in your hands, and helps you think about something aside from what's wrong with you. You practice over and over the one scale, or two-chord progressions, or three songs you know. You watch Bosnian folk bands on one of the three television stations you receive. You watch videotaped episodes of *Absolutely Fabulous* and *Noddy*. You listen to NPR through the Armed Forces Radio Network. You read.

Lying in bed, you hear the day's final call to prayer echo from the large mosque across the street. You listen to the distant rumble of the tram line. You listen to the cooing of the pigeons outside your window, and the occasional thwack of one of them being killed. You listen to your own uneven breath. And then you pass gratefully into sleep.

One day, walking home from work, you are suddenly desperate for nature. At home, when you have problems or issues to think over, or when you simply feel horrible for one reason or another, you go for a walk in the woods. But the woods here scare you with their land-mined paths, and your only access would be to have a taxi drop you off in the middle of nowhere. So you walk the roads. You walk for days, every afternoon after work.

You walk the main avenues that parallel the river on either side, the Marsala Titova and the Ubala Kulina Bana and the Skenderija. You walk among the ancient dark wood stalls of the Baščaršija, and the main pedestrian thoroughfare, the Ferhadija, closed off to cars and strutted down by well-turned-out Sarajevans happy to not be shot at. You walk past the first McDonald's in the country, which courted controversy when it opened by refusing to source its beef locally. You walk past buildings that range from neoclassical to Ottoman to Victorian to Edwardian. You walk past Mediterranean terra cotta and Soviet boxes and dark stone government ministry buildings and aluminum-trimmed 1970s prefabricated schools and Hapsburg stone fortresses. You walk away from the river, away from the broad avenues, into the neighborhoods in the low foothills, where the architecture changes from classical and art nouveau and purposed and designed to the more utilitarian, residential, flat-faced stucco homes and apartment buildings and narrow streets where stray dogs wander and children play soccer with blue-and-white balls that have been handed out by the United Nations.

You wander past scaffolded refurbishment projects and construction cranes and the big open pits of new construction. You wander up the winding streets built so steeply into the hillside that handrails have been installed to help pedestrians with their climbs and descents. You wander down street after street of gated yards and ferocious-looking guard dogs that bark at you as you pass. You wander past walls graffitied, and bullet-pocked and mortar-scarred and falling in. You wander past walls newly painted and landscaped yards and windowpanes with the manufacturers' stickers still affixed. You wander past other walls in other stages of construction, with exposed insulation panels and hollow timber frames and half-bricked walls and yards filled with sacks of cement and cement-stained wheelbarrows and shovels propped up against walls.

But it's not the same. You can't get away from yourself. You stand out, self-conscious with your Anglo features and an aid worker's khaki trousers and white button-down shirt, wandering through the Bosnian neighborhoods. As they pass, cars honk at you walking alone on the berm. "What the hell are you doing here?" they seem to scream, even though you know this is not true, that you have been welcomed along with everyone international, everyone foreign, everyone unconnected to the slow, cruel, methodical demolition of the city. You are symbols of the end of the war. And that's great. But you need nature. You need to find yourself in a place free from the impositions of humanity.

Then one afternoon, you wander in another direction, past the bombed-out library where the Obala Kulina Bana turns into the Bentbaša and follows the banks of the river Miljacka. The river flows east to west and enters the city after coming through a steep, rock-walled gorge. The road parallels the river through the gorge, and you find that you can walk this road around one bend and then another, and in no time, you are out of the city and in a grass-lined valley with steep rock walls and the river, which would be considered no more than a large stream where you come from, gurgling through the middle of it. You try to allow your heartbeat to slow and breathing to ease, but you are still concerned about the land mines you suspect lurk everywhere, so you stay on the worn asphalt and off the roadside gravel and grass.

Above you, built directly into the rock wall, a large, modern highway passes into a long tunnel, so that the traffic on it can be neither seen nor heard from below. You walk the old road next to the river as it weaves on, and at one particularly sun-filled spot, you see that a thin path has been worn through the grass and down to the water. You hesitate. You want to follow it, and feel quietly desperate to be beside the river. You stand still for a moment, contemplating, weighing.

And then you step off the road.

The path makes two little switchbacks as it descends the river bank, and at the bottom is a pebbled alluvial plain dotted with seedlings and tufts of new grass. A ring of boulders surrounds the blackened charcoal of an old fire. You sit down on one of the boulders, watch the river flow past, and feel a moment of peace.

The breeze blowing down the valley is beginning to cool, and the sun is descending and will soon fall behind the far wall of the canyon, leaving the valley in shadow. But before it does, there is time to appreciate its warmth and the way its light plays off of everything, glinting the edges of plant and stone. Here then, at last, is everything there is to be known. The leaves of this sapling flittering in the sunlight. This pebble, ground flat and smooth by the water's eternal flow. That cloud, high and cumulus and even now drifting out of view. The reality of these things, their tangibility made real by nothing more than your own observation of them. These interactions. These things that make up a life. These things that have made up lives for untold millennia. These things that compose this latest landscape through which you will pass, leaving behind no sign you were ever here.

ALICE DERRY
Horse Fantasies

for all the horses I didn't get to ride
the years of my girlhood in Montana.
I wasn't Terry Jo, the last child
and only daughter of a rancher
whose spread lay deep
in the sheepland steppe, forty miles
south of our little town.
Terry Jo, whose mother, like all
the ranchers' wives, moved to town
when snow closed the ranch roads,
so her child could go to school.
Alone there, in the cozy house,
lavished what she had on her,
mohair sweater sets and the pleated wool
coordinated skirts I longed for.
Singer in Teen Tones, skier on the weekends
she wasn't cheer leading (only in grades
I had a very slight edge) and summers,
horsewoman with a flair, riding crop,
tooled boots, and barrel racing—
her father, one of the royalty our town
bowed to, tanned, wiry sheepmen,
tainted, yes, of course,
by years of tearing lambs from unwilling
wombs, bossing the dark-skinned men
who sheared. Her father, sorry
for how he'd quarreled with his sons
until they left him,
one to doctoring, the other to drink,
taught her horseflesh, the saddle merely
an extension of four-legged motion.

I spoke the language of those ragged plains
as well as she who learned to sweep along them,
wind's love and not its resistance.

ELIZABETH EVANS
The Sky in the Glass-Topped Table

Before Edward stood and pointed his camera toward the table, Kelvyn hadn't noticed the way that the glass top held the islands' Bible-blue sky and the fat white puffs of cloud. That Edward noticed made her happy (she knew that the pictures he'd shot of her back in their adjoining cabins were of an entirely different order, even if he did call them art).

"Pretty!" she ventured.

No response. Kelvyn tried not to mind. She loved Edward. She knew that keeping expectations in check led to fewer disappointments, and so she concentrated on the breeze that blew over the deck and tickled the modest amount of skin exposed by the blue skirt Edward had asked her to wear. *Uncle Edward,* she was to call him during the cruise. The much chipped and painted-over surfaces of the ship's outer railings made her think of the flecks of scar that covered his back. "They're nothing," he'd said sharply when she once asked about them. Still, she supposed there must have been a case of acne, maybe so bad that the Edward who'd been her own age had to wear a T-shirt when he went swimming (it was a help to Kelvyn, now and then, to feel sad for the past that Edward never mentioned).

He moved a few paces across the deck. Not a big man, but beautiful with a profile that made her think of photographs she'd seen of ancient Greek busts, or maybe it was Roman. A large, fine nose, full but flat-surfaced lips. He already had made an impression on the other travelers, even in the quick-drying travel clothes that he had bought for the trip—so unlike his usual charcoal suits and the white shirts with starched collars and French cuffs. She wished that people knew he was her lover. Probably some did. Energy pumped through Edward, ticked the blue vein in his right temple. After sex, if Kelvyn laid her head on his upper arm, the noise of his muscles filled her ears, like something big and raising a ruckus in the far distance: lions, heavy machinery, oil derricks. She had felt a little spark of fear when she saw the age listed as they showed their passports in Guayaquil, but, then, the passport that he'd procured for her said that her name was Alexis Anne Burnham and that she was twenty-one instead of seventeen; so his age might be false too. His dark curly hair showed a few threads of silver, but there was lots of it, and fitted so tight to his skull that a crescent of magically paler skin appeared just beyond where the tan left off—an enchantment when you got up close, like a beam of sunlight discovered in deep woods.

Another man—squat in one of the Sea Beauty's heavy white robes—stepped out from the mini-gym. Mr. Brady? The reason for Edward's decision to join the cruise? The man let his eyes linger on Kelvyn's breasts. Edward maintained his smile of tender regard for the world. Later, he almost certainly would ask Kelvyn if she had been flirting, but he wouldn't really mean it. The smile—after almost three months, Kelvyn recognized his smile simply as his most consistent public expression. At his big house back in Dallas, he kept a boyhood photo of himself—ten years old, eleven?—and that beautiful young boy wore the exact same expression as he aimed a bow and arrow at an unseen target.

"Beautiful morning," Edward called to the man in the robe. The man nodded. Edward looked out over the small, dark swimming pool that the grinning Italian captain had explained during the "meet-and-greet" had formerly held the now-fancy ship's haul of herring (everyone was meant to laugh at the improbability of the beautiful ship's former life, and they did).

Out Edward's gaze went over the ship's white railings, across the teal blue sea to the horizon—though maybe he took in the bouncing Zodiacs that ferried one group to a beach famous for a certain variety of Darwin's mockingbirds, another to a snorkeling spot. Maybe he looked at nothing. Without turning, he asked Kelvyn, "What was it that you thought was so pretty?"

"In the tabletop?" she said. "Weren't you taking pictures of the clouds?"

"I was shooting the coffee cups, Alexis!" He laughed. She couldn't enjoy his laugh entirely since it might be just a matter of business, a demonstration of good nature for the benefit of the man in the white robe, but she did like to hear him call her Alexis. Before Kelvyn had dropped out of high school two years ago—shortly after her grandmother died and the State of Arizona sent Kelvyn and her brother Timmy to their Aunt Raina in Dallas—Kelvyn had been in Honors History with a long-legged Alexis who draped long, fuzzy scarves in look-at-me colors around her neck and swung down the halls of Tucson High with a beat-up leather case of what people said contained drawings. Her *portfolio*. Kelvyn's hapless parents had invented her name by combining theirs: Kelly and Melvyn. The pair drowned when Kelvyn was six; capsized a rowboat on a duck pond in Iowa that Kelvyn's grandmother always said they should not have been out on in the first place, both being drunk, neither knowing how to swim ("And praise the lord I had my wits about me and spared you being raised by that bitch Raina!").

What would be truly wonderful would be for Edward to sit down beside Kelvyn on the rattan loveseat and ask her about the books that the man at the Miami bookstore had recommended; or else tell her which of the ship's many activities he thought that they should consider that day. He was too good at playing the solicitous, though distracted, uncle. Just now, only the ache lighting up Kelvyn's pelvic muscles—a personal pink neon sign—reassured her of his love. She smiled at the thought that he could not control everything: the sky and clouds *would* turn up in some of his photographs of the coffee cups. Maybe that plain glass ashtray with its three cigarette butts would be in some of them too. If he hadn't been standing so close, she would have inspected the butts to see if any of them carried the tiny name of her grandmother's brand, "Old Gold." She would have taken one of those as a sign of good luck.

"Fucking freezing!" said the man who might be Mr. Brady and now had removed his terry robe and submerged one bare foot into the pool, where it appeared emerald green. A gold chain hung from his neck, and its small cross sat suspended on the mat of black hair on his chest. Edward made what Kelvyn was sure was just the right noise of amused sympathy while the man, one hand on the pool ladder, descended to chin level. He could draw people to him with his magical regard; then ignore them, keep them on edge, wanting more, and more would come again, if you were patient and you, too, had something that he wanted. Not your regard. Something else.

Back in Dallas, Edward had been very happy when he found out about Brady and the expedition to the Galapagos. "Five days! How often do you have a captive audience for five days?" Kelvyn wondered why Edward had picked Mr. Brady as his new "prospect." Edward already had plenty of money from a family that he refused to discuss. "Now that we have each other, why care about anyone else?" he'd said the time she asked if she could meet his relatives. She had felt it was permissible to ask because he just had told her—for the first time ever—that he loved her. His answer satisfied her for a while, but then, the next day, she started to think about her brother. She hoped that, eventually, Edward would let Timmy join them in Dallas. Edward's house in Dallas had too many rooms, windows so big that their floor-to-ceiling shades had to be operated by motors. Edward had so much money that foggy-windowed envelopes holding checks made out to him could spend weeks in the enormous blue-and-gold-striped pot he kept by the ten-foot-tall front door; envelopes holding checks mixed every which way with flyers for auto glass replacement, cable service, and supermarket specials. The same night that Edward first said he loved her—he'd finished a deal of some kind that day and so allowed himself a second scotch—he explained that money was not why he did what he did, which seemed to be convincing people they should invest in projects that didn't exist.

"Though they *could,* if the stars lined up right!" His muscular arms stretched wide on the top of his blond leather headboard had made her think of the crucified Jesus that hung in the bedroom of a childhood friend. Edward went on, "What I like is the trick of it. Now you see it, now you don't."

Before that night, she had been impressed whenever she over-heard him talking to people on the telephone or in his big home office. *Wanted to let you know that Spielberg and I are looking for backers.* Or, *I've got a sure bet with Time Warner if I can get a group together by Friday.* She didn't know how to ask if he made up everything, or some of it. Just before the two of them flew from Dallas to Miami to meet up with the expedition group, she'd woken up alone in the bedroom with the leather headboard. His bedroom, she'd always believed. She wandered through the moonlit house, searching for him. She felt certain that he would not like her calling out his name. Shadows of branches came through the giant windows and tangled on Edward's pale tile floors like briars that might trip her, tear her skin, or turn into snakes. Finally, behind a door upon which one wooden circle was carved within another—storage, he'd told her once—she found him asleep in a bed as big as the one with the leather headboard. She stopped just inside the doorway, feeling as if she'd stumbled into the hidden control center of a superhero, someone like Bruce Wayne/Batman. The room's only light came from a giant bubbling aquarium and the many pieces of electronic equipment that sat on tables and shelves. It put her in mind of the Dallas skyline at night, dark high-rises in which a few workers kept on a light, the glamorous passage of airplanes over the horizon.

She had known almost from the start that Edward depended on pills. Sometimes, he had to stay up around the clock to prepare for a meeting; if he was at home, he would let her bring him coffee and maybe a sandwich while he sat reading, taking notes on whatever topic was on his computer or in the books he'd ordered online. Once, she'd seen it was harvesting Peruvian lumber; another time, fabricating T-shirts in Bangladesh. *Fabricating* was easy, but she had to look up Bangladesh on the Internet (there were beautiful pictures of the art and ancient beautiful buildings and, at the time, she had wondered if they would go there sometimes and what Edward would pay workers if he manufactured T-shirts; the average annual income was seven hundred thirty-one dollars, and she thought he would surely pay much more than that). After Edward finished setting up a deal, sometimes, he needed a deep sleep. For that, he had a pill that made him hibernate; the first time she found him under that pill's spell, she was so frightened at being unable to wake him that she had made the mistake of running to the caretaker's house at the end of the long drive for help.

The night that she found him in the secret bedroom, she could tell he had taken one of the serious pills, because, in her haste to back out of the room without him seeing her—she could not have stood *his* knowing that she knew he kept secrets from her—she had knocked over a stack of plastic CD cases that stood at least a foot high. The cases made a terrible noise as they skittered across the tile floor, and Edward didn't even lift his head from his pillow while she set the things to rights.

On the edge of the ship's little pool—Kelvyn was startled by the discovery—a pretty dark-haired girl with a belly-button piercing that raised a tiny knuckle of well-tanned skin above her swimsuit bottom now had settled herself, and now she began to kick water in the direction of the hairy, shivering man. The man laughed. She called him "Dad." "How's the water, Dad?" she said. Edward had told Kelvyn that Brady was traveling with relatives—an infuriating discovery for Edward, who preferred to meet prospects while they were out of their usual orb (his word, "orb," round, elegant). The girl did not eliminate the possibility that the hairy man in the pool was Brady, but Brady was supposed to be a widower and grandfather. Kelvyn had pictured him older.

His voice low, Edward leaned over the glass-topped table and said, "Her top's too big."

Kelvyn felt sick at the idea of his looking at the girl's breasts, but at least what he'd said was a criticism. The girl couldn't have overheard, but she must have known something because her face turned bright pink. She grasped the lip of the pool with both hands, as if she were determined to keep herself there; then, in a gratifyingly un-pretty movement, she fumbled to her feet—in the process, barking her heel on the pool edge. She yelped with pain and Kelvyn felt a shudder of sympathy; still, she was glad to watch the girl scuttle off along the narrow slice of deck to the left. Maybe she headed to the wood-paneled library or the lounge stocked with round-the-clock snacks.

Kelvyn would have liked to go to the lounge. She couldn't get over the free food. Edward had laughed when he discovered that she'd stuck packets of string cheese and crackers and M&M's in her jacket after the meet-and-greet; she doubted that he ever had gone hungry.

A metal door clanged shut from the direction in which the girl had gone. Everyone assumed a high level of civilization on the ship. There were no keys and locks on the cabin doors. No safes to be found in the wooden wardrobes. Perfect respect reigned for "Do Not Disturb" signs. At the meet-and-greet, there was no warning against shoving on deck; or even the possibility of accidentally pushing someone over the rails. For a moment, Kelvyn imagined herself and that dark-haired girl fighting over Edward. Kelvyn was strong. After her Aunt Raina's boyfriend came after her the second time, Kelvyn started working out in the dirt-floored gym under the school basketball court. She got in a few good blows the next time the boyfriend put his arm around her neck; her suitcase was already packed and hidden in the empty dog-house out back. And she stayed strong. At Wendy's, she became the one who always volunteered to mop inside, sweep the parking lot, lift what needed lifting. She would almost certainly win—*prevail*—in a fight with the dark-haired girl, but shuddered at the thought of someone falling over the ship's railings, the sound of a final, distant splash. On dry land, scuffles had smaller consequences. Here, go overboard and you drowned. Here, there were sharks. Yesterday, seven had swum alongside the hull while the ship moved to its next anchorage. At first, Kelvyn couldn't see them. A friendly Asian American couple who had done the cruise twice before helped her, "Come right up to the rail, miss! Here's a good one!" and "Almost like powder! Not what you expect!" and then Kelvyn did make out the milky surprise swimming along in the blue.

The afternoon's choices included kayaking, scuba diving, a chance to walk among giant land tortoises, but when Edward and Kelvyn stopped by the hospitality desk after lunch and Edward saw that Brady had not signed up for any of them, he said, "We'll just stay on board." Kelvyn was disappointed.

The next morning—*Alexis Burnham* on the door, but Kelvyn's clothes in the mirrored wardrobe and Kelvyn's toiletries in the bathroom medicine cabinet—Kelvyn mentioned the upcoming trip to the research station where people studied the finches that first set Darwin thinking about evolution: "I read about it in the guide," she told Edward. "My grandma would have loved that. She loved evolution."

Edward laughed. "How do you 'love' evolution?"

She laughed back. "How could you not when it means you're on the outermost edge of everything that ever came before?"

He smiled. "Turn around, though."

She turned around. He'd had her change from the pink lacy top that he'd picked for breakfast into a clay-colored camp shirt almost identical to his own, ugly venting in the armpits and all. He'd bought both. He'd bought all of the clothes in the wardrobe. She's been wearing stuff from a bag she'd found leaned up against a Goodwill donation box the day they met at the art museum in Dallas (Free Tuesday, Kelvyn off work from Wendy's). A group of children led by a museum guide had surrounded Edward and Kelvyn as each of them looked at a painting (Paul Klee, pinkish, dreamy). The children pressed the two of them shoulder to shoulder. It wasn't Edward's good looks that caused Kelvyn to stay put after the group moved off, but her delicious sense that he had supported her for a moment, took her weight entirely. "Do you have a favorite?" he asked her. Magic. Because she was afraid that her speaking out loud would break the spell, she had signaled for him to follow her to the dimly lit gallery that held an altar made up of small paintings of Jesus, the Virgin, saints fighting dragons, each surrounded by a small gold frame.

"It's my favorite too," he said, then added, after taking a deep breath, "now that you've shown it to me." To make certain that he understood who she was, she spoke then. She explained that it wasn't religion that made her like the altar, but the idea of the altar as a giant picture made up of many little ones. After that, even though she wore the brown pants of her Wendy's uniform and clothes from the donation box—a T-shirt proclaiming "I AM a rocket scientist!" and running shoes so dried out and gray with wear that they reminded her of dead lizards—he took her to lunch at a high-rise restaurant with white linen and silver, as fancy as restaurants that, previously, she had glimpsed only in movies and on television. He nodded when she told him that she was going to be a writer. He did not think she was silly for preferring George Eliot over Jane Austen, even though her grandmother always had insisted that Austen was superior, given that Eliot had studied Austen's work.

He knew that George Eliot was a woman.

He took her to a park with fountains and white stone columns wrapped in vines with purple flowers that smelled like grape gum. For tea—*tea!*—later that day, they went to a place as fancy as the place where they had eaten lunch. Then he took her to a hotel that was not quite so nice, turned her upside down, shook the brains out of her head.

She had wondered if that was something like what he did to his prospects; turned them stupid with yearning to be part of whatever he had in mind.

That Edward chose you was part of his appeal. That he did not need you—somehow that worked in his favor too. She had been pleased by her first impression that the two of them had been thrown together as fellow art-lovers; thrilled when he later admitted, his hooded eyelids lowered, that he had entered the museum only because he'd seen her go inside as he drove past.

The ship's dining room was almost as nice as the restaurants in Dallas that Edward had taken her to their first day together. The men in white jackets and shirts and black bowties seemed honored by their service. There was a blaze of white linen, polished wood, and brass railings that sparkled and shone. The windows contained nothing but perfect views. On this particular afternoon, the next island seemed a pink cloud, no more substantial than cotton candy. On occasion, the big room's low ceiling—the only reminder of its days as a fishing boat—did make Kelvyn feel odd, as if she wore a hat with its brim pulled too low. Still, she worked hard to look as pleasant as Edward while they crossed the room. She supposed that he worked too. She knew that he was fuming. He had counted on the policy of open seating as the perfect way to become acquainted with Brady, but, as at every other meal, waiters now pushed together a series of tables for the Brady family, a tribe of what had turned out to be tall blondes (one of them already had arrived, a big-eared teenager who gave Kelvyn a look both nervous and derisive while Edward pulled out her chair).

Edward was frustrated. She understood that one of his ways of getting close to a prospect was to pick up the tab for an expensive evening after they'd "accidentally" met at a vacation spot. The cruise—the *expedition,* the company called it—included meals, so there was no dinner tab to pick up, and Kelvyn thought that, back in the cabin, she might suggest that he send a bottle of wine—wine cost extra—to the Brady table that night.

She had helped him pick out gifts for his prospects' wives after a few of his trips. The gifts were the second step, he'd explained to her after they'd been together for a month or so. "Then, a few weeks later, I call and say I've got business in his city and suggest a get-together."

Recently, he had asked her to go on several trips. The first one was to Des Moines, Iowa, which wasn't far from where she'd been born, but she'd mostly stayed in the hotel that looked out on the interstate and cornfields. On the airplane, flying from Iowa back to Dallas, he'd said that it would be easier for her to appear in public with him when she was older (thrilling that he thought of the two of them in the future!). San Francisco was nice. He had a man—a person called a *concierge*—set up a plan for places that Kelvyn could visit (the de Young Museum, the Japanese Tea Garden, the Garden of Shakespeare's Flowers) and a cab to take her "about." *We'll get a cab to take you about.* Edward talked like that, the way that people talked in books, the way that Kelvyn sometimes talked in her head. They had gone to Hawaii too. There had been something unpleasant—well, Hawaii was wonderful, of course. She had her own fringed cabana on a white sand beach. While Edward met with his prospect, Larry, she swam in the turquoise waves. She walked up and down the sandy beach and collected beach glass worn to perfect, gauzy blues and greens. Whenever a boy approached her—

to keep things simple—she suggested that he was in real danger, saying in a low voice, *My father has people watching. Keep going.*

Hawaii was the only time that she ever had met a prospect. The prospect and Edward had appeared, two silhouettes backlit by the bright beach beyond her cabana. They smelled like too many rum drinks. The prospect wore an ash-colored toupee that had slid forward unmistakably during his afternoon of drinking with Edward, and she wished that she could find a way to tell him so until she understood that he thought that it was funny to act polite to her. "Pleased to meet you, madam," he said and bowed as he left the cabana. Edward had hardly seemed like himself, wearing a golfer's visor stenciled with a cartoon Charlie Brown, and grinning in a lazy, unfamiliar way, laughing too loud.

In the hotel room, later, she asked if he'd been pretending to be drunk, for the sake of the prospect. He stood up so fast from his chair that she thought for a moment that he meant to hit her, and she raised her arms over her face, but he only hurried across the room and began to fiddle with the thermostat, there. He stood with his ear cocked toward the thing, as if he waited for it to tell him something. He was still standing there when he said, "Larry thought you were beautiful. He'd like to come up to the room and see you." He tapped the thermostat with his fingernail. "Of course," he added, "I'd stay. You wouldn't have to worry." Very fast, in order to let him know that it never would occur to her to guess that his words might mean what they possibly meant, she said, "I know how to make conversation, silly!" but her voice came out wrong, like the manic squawk of a hard-haired lady who'd hawked discount mattresses on the television in Tucson. Also, Kelvyn never had called Edward *silly,* or anything remotely like it. His face was blank when he went to open the sliding door to the balcony. Still blank when he went back to the thermostat and tapped it again. As if he had forgotten Larry, he picked up the remote control and he sat down on the edge of hotel's big king-size bed and turned on the television. After a while, he dropped back on the bed, and he fell asleep that way, his feet still on the floor. She took off his shoes and the Charlie Brown visor. Since she doubted they'd be going anywhere for dinner, she ate the package of Goldfish Crackers and fancy chocolates she found in the room's refrigerator. She felt hollow. She had thought he might be growing tired of her until he suggested she come on the Galapagos tour.

*

One of the smiling Ecuadoran waiters set down a basket of rolls whose warmth was guarded by a heavy linen napkin, twin to the napkin that Kelvyn stroked in her lap. There would be six rolls, enough for all of the people who eventually might fill the table, and the waiter would bring more, if asked. After the man backed away with a bow, Edward leaned closer to Kelvyn. Sometimes, when they were in public, he said funny nonsense syllables, just now, something like *Dee-da-dee-purpurlada.* He nodded. Smiled his smile. Sat back in his chair as if he were satisfied that he had clarified a point.

She smiled. "How about I tell you about what I'm reading, though?"

"We're satisfied to enjoy each other's company in silence," he said, and then he was smiling at the man they now knew was Brady. Edward had figured out ways to talk to Brady a few times. Brady was old, rangy, a tall man with wrinkled arms as tan and shiny as pretzel sticks, flyaway white hair, bright blue eyes. His cabin was 112, just down from theirs, 118 and 120. Brady nodded at Edward as he took a seat at his family's extended table. He smiled at Kelvyn with tawny, raggedy teeth that must have been straightened and bleached in his handsome offspring and their children.

"Excuse me for a moment, won't you, Alex?" It seemed to be the most natural thing in the world for Edward to push back his chair and step over to the neighboring table. Brady and the other men rose. The Brady females—all creamy linen and fat gold earrings and bangles— stirred themselves slightly at the same moment that Edward signaled with his hands, *no, no,* and the entire group gratefully relaxed back into their chairs. All except Brady himself, who stepped away from the table and smiled at whatever Edward told him.

Kelvyn knew that the warm rolls under the napkin would be delicious, with a crust both crisp and chewy. When she met Edward, she was living in an unfurnished room over a bakery, and if the arrival of the bakers didn't wake her at three, the smell of bread did at four. She tried to go to sleep very early; still, she sometimes fell asleep during her bus rides to Wendy's.

"May we join you?"

She startled. A man and woman, probably Edward's age, stood with their hands resting on the backs of two of the table's vacant chairs. "Of course," she said.

They had spent the morning snorkeling! they said. A happy pair. The pink of the woman's cheeks glowed right through her tan, and though her mouth stayed open in a constant oval that revealed her narrow, protuberant teeth—rabbitish—she was pretty. The man was maybe interesting to look at, his face hollowed out; he had khaki-colored hair and skin, khaki clothes covered with pockets and grommets, like a host on a nature show. Women were usually more attractive than their mates; Kelvyn supposed that she and Edward were close, though she understood that she had youth on her side.

"I'm reading that same book," Kelvyn told the woman, "*The Reluctant Mr. Darwin.*"

The woman glanced down at the paperback sitting under her big sunglasses. "Really?"

Kelvyn ignored the *really*. Even in grade school, she'd had teachers who disapproved of her being smart. "I like the way he—Quammen—assumes you already believe in evolution."

The woman nodded, then winked at the man, but here was Edward, resuming his seat, smiling. He was happy now, which meant that Kelvyn could be happy too. "I was just asking Joe Brady if his group will be taking the Machu Picchu extension," he said to the couple. "How about you two? Are you going on?"

They nodded. "It was on my bucket list!" the woman said. "I probably shouldn't mention that, though, when it's on lists more important than mine." She cut her eyes toward the entryway where one of the three passengers who always wore kerchiefs tied tight to their skulls stood waiting, looking down at her toes as she wiggled them in their open sandals. At the meet-and-greet, Kelvyn had assumed that the women in kerchiefs were members of a religious group—it seemed to her an inward flame burned in them—but Edward said, no, they'd probably had cancer and chemotherapy, and this trip was a special wish fulfilled. How healthy all of them looked! None of them appeared pale or underweight or frightened. Kelvyn hoped that this meant that they were cured. One of the women traveled with a husband and children.

Edward told the couple that he wished he could go on the Machu Picchu trip too, "but intriguing projects call me on to New York and LA."

The woman smiled. "We were talking to your"—she cocked her head toward Kelvyn.

"My niece. Alexis."

"About that book I've been reading." Kelvyn pointed to the paper-back. "I'm at this part where Darwin's trying to see whether plants can move around the world. One experiment—he killed pigeons and kept them in salt water for months, which was about how long he figured it would take for the ocean to carry the body of a pigeon to—I think it was South America. With currents and things. From England. Darwin lived in England."

Edward smiled at the man and woman: Of course, they all knew that. Still, Kelvyn went on, "He took seeds out of their gizzards and he planted them and some of them grew!"

"We don't know how she got so smart," Edward said. "It doesn't run in the family."

The couple laughed, and then she did too, and there were other nice things that Edward said. Alex was a fine student. On the honor roll. A fine young writer. Edward never had read her writing, but Kelvyn still felt so pleased that her leg bounced under the table. Then, even better, after lunch, holding fast to ropes on the top of the bouncing Zodiacs—looking funny in their bright life vests, smiling at the other people as the waves splashed them—they went on an expedition. As soon as they stepped out of the Zodiac and onto the island's black volcanic rock, they encountered the giant, ponderous iguanas, their black-and-red skin sloughing off in great red sheets—hideous, but on the same black rocks were orange-and-blue crabs called Sally Go Lightlys doing a delicate dance. The animals of the Galapagos were famously fearless. Neither the lizards nor a pair of sea lions moved as the tour group walked by, headed up a sandy path that eventually wound its way to a colony of albatross at the top of high cliffs that provided the requisite drop for any bird ready to set its grand cargo of self in flight.

"Glorious!" said an old lady who traveled with her son's family, and she smiled at Kelvyn, and Kelvyn nodded. Glorious. On the way back to the Zodiac, to her delight, a blue-footed booby gave a desultory peck at the rim of her sandal when she passed the giant egg that the bird had laid in the middle of the sandy path, the Islands' remoteness having reduced the birds' instinct for nest-building to the gathering of three pieces of dried grass.

"That was glorious!" she said to Edward when they were back on the Sea Beauty. He nodded. "It was," he said, and, that night, after dinner, he was all for their joining the rest of the group in the lounge to view the footage that the ship's photographer, a tall, friendly Australian, had shot so far.

"I'll be making up a DVD shortly after you head home and you'll all get a copy," he said, and Kelvyn tapped Edward's knee, just then, because there Edward was, on each of the room's several large screens, shooting his own photos of the scowling iguanas on the black rocks. Disappointing to Kelvyn that the only way that she could have been identified in the group was by her broad-brimmed yellow sunhat, but, then, they still had another full day of touring. She took a second of the slushy rum drinks from the silver tray carried by the waiter passing between the lounge's swiveling easy chairs and tiny tables, and neither he nor Edward made a face of objection. Even though her passport said that she was twenty-one, she felt pleased to be so daring—until the lights came up and she spied Brady's big-eared grandson lifting an entire tray of the drinks from the bar and carrying it to the couch beyond the pool table where the five passengers close to Kelvyn's age always sat, clearly determined to stay away from adults and small children.

"Excuse me, Alexis," Edward said, "but I want to have a word with the photographer." No one else might have noticed but she saw the snag in his expression, like he was a fish on a hook being reeled in. The footage. He wouldn't want to be in the footage. He'd gotten rid of the snagged look by the time he reached the photographer. She swiveled her chair slightly so that she could see the teenagers at the back of the room. They were laughing. One boy tapped the head of a girl—the dark-haired girl from that first day of the pool—with the tip of a cue stick. They made Kelvyn nervous, but she was ready to smile if they looked her way, and when Edward came back and lowered himself back into his chair, she whispered, "Would it be smart if I said hi to the people by the pool table? Like, my peers?"

He smiled, his eyes on the closest screen, now showing shots of other expeditions (Antarctica, the Amazon, the fjords of Norway). "Peers? I suspect they're high-school kids."

She supposed that might be the reason that, the next morning—sounding very cheerful, as if he talked about another of the cruise's many opportunities for adventures—he explained that she would be staying in the cabin for the rest of the day. He fiddled with his camera while he talked. He wore a shirt he'd bought for the trip, a thing made of a turquoise blue fabric that dried almost as fast as it got wet. "You're sick," he said. "The sea got to you. Or maybe the rum drinks?"

He smiled at her then, so she didn't make any objections. Yesterday had been *glorious*. Maybe tomorrow would be *glorious* too. Tomorrow's schedule offered reef snorkeling with the possibility of swimming alongside penguins and sea lions. She climbed back into bed while Edward fetched the ship's nurse, a woman with a cropped, mannish haircut and a bulge lapping the waist of her white pants. "Your uncle says maybe you had too much rum last night?" she murmured while slipping her stethoscope between the buttons of crisp pajamas bought specifically for this trip. Hard to act sick in those pajamas. As a little kid, Kelvyn had read every one of the Tucson library's collection of Nancy Drew books, and the crisp pajamas made her feel like Nancy, upright, *perky*. She looked over the woman's shoulder at Edward, stationed by the door that joined his cabin to hers. She did not answer the nurse's question about the rum. *He* taught me that was possible, she thought, and felt proud. After the nurse left, as if he had come to think of Kelvyn as actually sick, Edward seemed concerned. He went to the desk and requested that the PA system to her room be silenced so she could sleep. He brought her a glass of orange juice and hung the Do Not Disturb sign on her door. Seated at the end of her bed, he rubbed her feet. In all her life, no one ever had rubbed her feet. She couldn't believe the pleasure.

Something like the moon—the moon wasn't right, but a blinding brightness, a bulbous curve that pressed impossibly upward, inside of her and outward and on forever, it was unbearable, but what followed was worse in its own way: endless dimpled beige dust. The sense of lack made her wish she were dead.

A roar came, then, so big that it allowed her to wonder—words— "Did my eardrums break?" at the same moment that she became aware she lay on something, no longer participated in the dimpled dust. She commanded nearly useless fingers to inch across whatever it was, a flatness, paper, but softer. That went beneath the burning that announced itself, a sewing machine whose thread was fire stitched and stitched into her rectum. The roar subsided, but not the pain, which brought her around to the memory of the ship.

There were footsteps. Above her and in the hall. She made out a muffled voice. "Two-ten departure! Meet at Door B! Two-ten departure! Door B!"

She could not put off opening her eyes forever.

Still in the cabin, the narrow bed, the pajamas. Only truly sick now. In order to get to her feet, she had to hang onto the reading light attached to the wall, force pain into a propellant stronger than her stupor. She called out, "Edward?" Balloons, pale gray and pink and yellow, rose up around her while she caromed across the cabin to the shared door.

"Edward?" The door was ajar and she pushed it open, but the cabin was empty, the bed made. She backed up. Suppose there had been an evacuation. She slid her way along the wall to the spot where her life-vest hung alongside the Sea Beauty bathrobe.

So heavy! The effort required to remove the vest from its hook made her weep. And the impossible straps and rings—

She barely made it to the toilet, collapsed onto her knees, held the rim of the bowl while she vomited again and again—and there was no time for this! She raised her head and called, "I'm in here! Anybody!"

It was easiest to crawl to the door. There she hauled herself to standing with the help of the knob. The corridor was empty when she stepped out, but she heard music. She moved toward it. Room 112. *Joe Brady,* read the card on the closed door. The music in Room 112 was not so loud that she couldn't recognize the sound of Edward's laughter.

"I help, please?"

The voice belonged to a tiny, round woman, dark cheeks bunched up in a smile full of fear or worry—one of the Ecuadoran maids who'd appeared from who knew where. She remained at what she seemed to have decided was a safe distance from Kelvyn, maybe ten feet off.

Kelvyn shook her head and started down the corridor in the direction of the alcove for Door B. Pain made her slow, necessity made her fast. She lurched.

As was typical during the day, most of the tags showing whether passengers were on board (left) or off (right) had been moved to the right. The tags for 112, 118, and 120 remained on the left.

Their first morning on board, while she and Edward unpacked their bags, she had watched Edward's reflection in her open wardrobe's mirror—Edward slipping his camera into the pink cardboard box that had held the large tube of sunblock he'd purchased for the trip.

She found the pink box, now, on the bottom shelf of his medicine cabinet, behind several of the miniature bottles of blue-green mouthwash that the maid sets on the sink's rim each morning, along with miniature bottles of rosemary shampoo and cucumber moisturizer. After she removed the camera and the extra memory card stashed with it, she put the box back and replaced the bottles of mouthwash. There wasn't time to stop and inspect what she saw in the wastebasket alongside Edward's toilet—one of the ship's white washcloths, wrung out, but dark—or the smears she saw on her sheets when she climbed back into the bed.

Under the covers, shivering and wishing that she could be sick in the toilet again, she pressed the button that turned on Edward's camera with a brief, delicate whir.

At first, all that she saw was a confusion of cloudy white—the blizzard raised by the sheets around her swinging into view—but she remembered how Edward pressed the arrow that allowed for reviewing stored pictures and movies.

Mr. Brady came up immediately, already in action, his parrot-covered shirt flopping, his trousers down around his knees while he pounded against what could have been just a heap of bedding, but then Edward entered the shot and helped the old man flip over what turned out to have breasts—almost immediately obscured by Brady's thrusting hips and the way that Edward's legs blocked the viewer from seeing the head that the tilt of his arms suggested he held steady for Brady's thrusts—

She expelled the card. Her unstable mix of terror and sorrow—plus whatever Edward had put in her orange juice—caused small explosions behind her eyes. She supposed that the other memory card held yesterday's blue-footed boobies, albatrosses, iguanas. The sharks swimming alongside the ship's hull. A sunset or sunrise. The white coffee cups in the sky on the glass-topped table.

She could not turn the brass latch on the porthole cover. A jingling filled her ears after she tried—like the shivery sound of a light bulb shaken once its filament has burned out. Was that what she was? A sob burst out of her. The captain had told the travelers during the meet-and-greet—in the merry way in which he told them almost everything—that the cost of air-conditioning the ship required that he ask them, "Please not to use the portholes! I think you find plenty fresh air on deck!" She bore down harder, not breathing for fear the sound might make her miss Edward's opening the door.

It turned. She swung the heavy cover up over her head, let its weight rest on the back of her skull while she worked her arm out through the opening. Her pitch was strong enough that she did not hear any sound of the camera or the memory cards hitting against the hull.

To practice composure, even though she still felt stupefied, once she had latched the porthole and gotten back into the bed, she kept her eyes open. She would smile sleepily when Edward came in. She would carry her escape deep inside her, like the seeds that had traveled Darwin's hypothetical thousands upon thousands of miles by mode of lumps of decaying flesh, and still remained viable. A good word that she had learned the meaning of through context: *Viable.* Tomorrow morning, they would fly back to Guayaquil. Edward would be worried about the camera, but unable to mention its loss to her or anyone else. In Miami, though, once they separated from the polite members of the tour, he might feel differently. She would disappear as soon as they landed in Miami, lose herself in the crowds on a trip to the ladies room.

The idea of starting over, alone, hardly frightened her now—though her heart did ache: To think that Edward never had known her; never understood that she was a person who still had far to go in the world.

DENISE DUHAMEL
Reading

Sometimes I read pages of books without retaining anything.
I am thinking about my own drama and caesura
until I come across a word like *creosote,* which seems familiar
but I have to look up. When I go to the dictionary, I realize
I am wondering who will bury me and where,
going over the time I was almost hit by a car on A1A.
It was dark, and he'd left me in the parking garage
saying, "I'll go ahead and get us a table." He meant
inside of Le Tub where there was always a long wait.
I stood in front of the Master Meter with my fistful of coins.
"OK," I said. What if that had been the end, that flattened smack, of me?
He would have looked up from the menu to the sirens—
their wail and red pulsing light—and it might have taken him
a moment to realize I was the one on the ground.
The thing about reading is that your mind might wander
to imagine the author sitting long enough
and silent enough to recall such a moment, so intimate
she never even mentioned it to her date.
The driver who almost hit me had forgotten
to turn on his headlights. And what about the intimacy
of writing itself? Each finger pad on a key, or the pen's whisper
into paper. What makes us do it, relive instead of live, go back
and forward in time? It's like dancing
to empty chairs in an empty room of a closed bar,
your shimmery ghost there long after you've left.
Only a few people will come to the dive
where you once danced, or turn to the page
where you left some marks, look at the words you wrote.
Fewer still will read them. Then a mixture
of vanity and humility if a stranger understands.
Or looks up a word she'd forgotten she knew.

Writing

There are feelings I would rather not have,
so I avoid certain types of texts and images—
particularly pornography. Sometimes I think this makes me
a better person, but, in actuality, it also makes me a coward.
Am I so afraid I'll enjoy some ridiculously sexist fantasy?
I'm not sure what I'd do with the ugliness
I'd find inside me. *Don't you ever just want to shut off*
your brain? Deb asks. Yes.
In fact, I try shutting off my brain,
but when I do, I just fall asleep. The endless filter,
the endless scrubbing of my sins through dream.
In all writing, something is withheld. You might say,
in pornography, what is withheld is love.
Once Deb grew so skinny (eating disorder)
that she hoped to dive and disappear into a straw
like the model she saw in the diet soda commercial.
But now here she is telling me we have to be less rigid,
her favorite phrase—*So what?*
Who is the candy? Who is the one gobbling it up?

REBECCA MORGAN FRANK
What Is Left Here

Out in the open, there is a cowshed.
There are the expected gaps and hornets.

Here lives our story, where we used to meet—
You smelled like hay, were always listening

to some other sound, the buzzing of your own
ideas chasing us down. You began building

a staircase out of thorny branches, then a vest
out of found nests. An angel emerged

from bones and wrenches; a vulture out of junkyard
parts flew in the rafters. Soon the shed was full

of your configurations. You made me pose,
sculpted a rusted wire shadow of me. Sometimes

I saw you watching her while kissing me.
I knew: who wouldn't want to love a mind

like that? I knew: I was part of something.
Now I catalog your works, care for minutiae

of preservation, communications. Loving you
is never over, even with you gone. You knew

you shaped me here, under gap-leaked light.
Amidst all the other figures of your making.

JENNIFER HAIGH

Sublimation

Every evening after the network news, Dolly and her son watch "Jeopardy!" The habit dates back thirty years, to Bruce's moody adolescence. Naturally shy, he was prone even then to sudden, awkward displays of confidence. "Jeopardy!" let him show off his worldly knowledge, which for a boy who'd seldom left the state of Maryland—who wouldn't leave the house if he could help it—was vast indeed.

Now that Bruce has moved back home, they tune in as though nothing has changed, though of course everything has. He is forty-six now, marginally employed; Dolly a year shy of eighty and in questionable health. In three decades, they and the world have transformed unrecognizably. "Jeopardy!" is exactly the same.

He sits in his old spot, cross-legged on the divan; Dolly in the plaid armchair once reserved for her husband. Ten years widowed, she no longer considers it Tony's chair, no longer—it's terrible—considers Tony much at all, though he's right there on top of the piano, Dolly and Tony dressed in the usual way, a larger version of the couple on the cake. The wedding photo is flanked on either side by high-school graduation portraits of Bruce and Andrew. Both boys resemble their father but, oddly, look nothing alike.

"What is mitosis?" Bruce asks the television.

The familiar rhythm is comforting, each clue answered with a question. Dolly's memory is sluggish since the stroke, her mind like an old car that needs warming up. Bruce answers aloud before she can even process the clues.

"Who is Evel Knievel?"

"What was Biafra?"

"What is 'Rock Around the Clock'?"

Occasionally, he gets an answer wrong—answering *mitosis,* for example, instead of *meiosis.* Dolly pretends not to notice. At school the nuns called him gifted, praised his careful penmanship, his quick arithmetic, his memory for names and dates. Who knew then that the world was about to change in unsettling ways, the whole human race plugged into computers morning, noon, and night?

That handwriting and arithmetic would become obsolete and knowledge itself would lose its value, once any half-bright teenager could, with a few keystrokes, conjure it from the air.

At the commercial, she goes into the kitchen to mix their highballs. One drink a day is good for her cholesterol, according to *Prevention* magazine. Married to an industrious drinker, she'd been, not coincidentally, a teetotaler until her seventies. Now she looks forward to the reliable festivity of her nightly cocktail—a fair reward, at her age, for getting through another day.

On a pretty tray, she arranges the drinks—hers mostly ginger ale, a stronger one for Bruce—and brings them out to the living room. "That one's yours, dear."

She always calls him *dear* in the evenings. It's easier, somehow, than addressing him by name.

"Thanks, hon." Bruce drinks deeply, leaving a bloom of lipstick on the rim of his glass. The new wig is an improvement over his old one, closer to his natural color. She never had the heart to tell him he was unconvincing as a blonde.

"Who was Pericles?" he asks the television. "What is the Knesset?"

Bruce and *Dolly* are the names the world calls them, names they have always called each other. At home in the evening, behind closed doors, they are *dear* and *hon.*

She imagines Tony watching them from atop the piano, young Tony staring out from the photo at what they've become.

Bruce sleeps in his boyhood room, unchanged all these years: the Hardy Boys and science fair trophies, the plaid curtains and matching counterpane. A temporary arrangement, they told each other at first, until Dolly got back on her feet. The stroke was, knock wood, a mild one; her doctor prescribed blood thinners, and in a week she felt perfectly herself. When Bruce showed no sign of leaving, Dolly understood that her recovery wasn't the point; that her son, too, had been stricken: laid off after many years at the Post Office, the *good government job* that once seemed so sure.

His life hasn't turned out as expected. Nobody's does. Even Dolly, who got exactly what she'd aimed for—the handsome husband, the home and children—was unprepared for the deep loneliness of marriage, the heartbreak of motherhood. How briefly her boys would need her, how quickly they'd disappear into lives totally separate from hers and become like all the other people in the world.

The exact husband she'd wanted, tall and handsome. During their courtship and early marriage, he carried her around like a doll. Her given name—Barbara Jean—didn't, in his opinion, suit her. When they married, Dolly Tobin was who she became.

Their son's habit isn't news to her, not really; though she always imagined he'd outgrow it. Children left everything behind, eventually. Her attic is full of board games and sports equipment and Boy Scout uniforms, a veritable zoo of stuffed animals she can't bear to throw away.

She'd been an indulgent mother, no question—happiest when the boys were babies, helplessly lovestruck at their round cheeks and silky hair. Almost from birth, their differences were apparent. Andrew was all boy—boisterous and competitive, fond of roughhousing. Bruce, three years younger, preferred indoor play. On summer afternoons, he and Dolly watched the stories. Bruce knew the plots better than she did: the secret affairs and paternity scandals, the amnesias and kidnappings, the flamboyant villains who came back from the dead.

In those years, she earned pin money selling Avon cosmetics, spent happy hours browsing the catalogs with Bruce at her side. They had a grand time sampling the products together—on the Q.T., always. The secrecy was part of the fun.

Now Avon, if it still exists, is sold over the computer like everything else; and housewives, if they still exist, have better things to do with their time. Andrew's wife is a podiatrist who raises two children on the side, when she isn't looking at strangers' feet.

The sparkly eye shadows and trial-size lipsticks, in white plastic cases the size of bullets. It all seemed harmless when Bruce was eight or nine.

Not to his father, of course. Even then, Tony wouldn't have understood. Little Bruce seemed to grasp this intuitively. When Tony came home from the mill at 4:30, Bruce's face was already scrubbed clean.

Later that evening, Andrew calls. He does this more often since Bruce moved in, as though the particulars of their mother's life, the doctor's appointments and geriatric social engagements, have suddenly become interesting to him. The calls are brief, five minutes of terse questions that make Dolly nervous for no reason, since Andrew never remembers anything she tells him. She doesn't blame him, really. Why should he keep track of her colonoscopies and Legion of Mary luncheons, when she can barely remember them herself?

Andrew is a fast talker. He is a type of lawyer that never appears in court, just goes to meetings and makes phone calls. He ignores her question about the weather in Atlanta. "Ma, this will have to be quick. Let me talk to Bruce."

Dolly glances into the living room. Bruce is playing solitaire on the coffee table, his wig slightly askew. "He's in the shower."

From the living room Bruce blows her a kiss.

"He was in the shower the last time I called." A tapping on the line, Andrew fidgeting with something. He is incapable of sitting still. "What does he do all day, anyway?"

Dolly lowers her voice. "Now, Andrew. He works."

"At Radio Shack? Give me a break."

She takes the cordless phone down to the basement. "Twenty hours a week. Plus, he's a big help around the house." In defending one son against the other, she sometimes makes statements that aren't precisely true. For example: in the last ten months, Bruce hasn't cooked a meal or washed a dish, though he does sometimes drive her to the Food Circus, or some other place she used to travel by bus.

She tries a new subject. "Did Zoe get my graduation card?" Andrew's stepdaughter is a rich source of material: overweight, rebellious, an erratic student. Dolly wonders, but hasn't asked, if the girl is on drugs.

"Oh, yeah. Thanks, Mom." Unusually, Andrew hesitates. "I might as well tell you, Zoe's had some trouble. Drinking and—other things."

Aha, Dolly thinks.

"She's in a program now. We're hoping she's out of the woods."

At that moment the music starts, softly at first. The call has gone longer than usual; Bruce must have assumed she was off the phone.

Andrew, luckily, seems not to hear it. "Actually, that's why I called. Janet"—the podiatrist—"is worried, we both are, about what's going to happen when she gets home."

Bruce has a heavy touch. The old piano vibrates the floor. The song is one Dolly and Tony danced to years ago; what on earth is it called? As usual, she remembers all the words except the two or three critical ones.

"Her friends are a bunch of burnouts. If she's hanging around with them, she doesn't stand a chance." Another pause. "Maybe she could spend the summer with you."

"Here?" It is a startling notion. Dolly has never quite grasped her exact relationship to this girl, who was already twelve years old when Andrew married the podiatrist and who seemed uninterested in acquiring an additional grandmother. Still, Dolly sends, at Christmas and birthdays, Hallmark cards with twenty-dollar bills tucked inside. That these gifts are never acknowledged is perhaps not Zoe's fault. Children aren't born with manners. Dolly blames the podiatrist.

"She could, I don't know, take a class at Hopkins. Is that the piano?"

Oh, dear.

"I suppose so," Dolly says.

"So Big Bruce is out of the shower. Put him on, will you?"

Dolly takes the phone upstairs. Bruce, too vain for glasses, leans back slightly on the piano bench, his neck craned at an odd angle so he can read the music. Dolly lays a hand on his silky shoulder. "Sorry to bother you, dear. Andrew wants to say hello."

His eyes, rimmed with black liner, go wide like Charlie Chaplin's. His shoulder tenses beneath her hand.

"He heard the piano," she whispers.

Bruce takes the phone. He turns away from Dolly and speaks in his gruff daytime voice. "Hey, man. How you been?"

The song is called "Begin the Beguine."

There were clues, she sees in retrospect. Soon after Bruce moved in, her mailbox was flooded with junk mail, catalogs for ladies' jewelry and lingerie and once, large-size shoes. The mailing labels read B TOBIN— B for Barbara, she assumed.

Once, after she'd already washed everything in his hamper, she caught him doing a load of laundry. The machine was set to the delicate cycle, though her son lived in jeans and old sweatshirts, store-brand, from Ross' Big and Tall.

Still she'd never have made the connection, would never have learned the truth at all, if not for her own forgetfulness. Every Wednesday afternoon, while Bruce is at Radio Shack, she takes the No. 12 bus across town for her wash and set. Afterward, she plays cards at Pine Grove, where a number of her old friends have been parked by their children. It's not bad, for one of those places. On nice days, she takes a slow walk in the garden with Ida Binder, who has early Alzheimer's but can still get around.

One day last September, Dolly skipped the visit to Pine Grove. Waiting for the bus, she felt flushed, lightheaded. The afternoon was unseasonably hot, the air heavy with summer smells: ripe trash, melting tar, the harbor simmering like a stew of spoiled fish. She arrived at the beauty parlor feeling queasy. An hour later, sitting under the hairdryer, she understood that she'd forgotten her morning pills.

Panic washed over her: what stood between her and another, more crippling stroke, but her Coumadin and Lopressor? She took the first bus home, counting off miles and minutes. Salvation was waiting in the amber plastic bottles, lined up neatly in the cabinet above the kitchen sink.

To her surprise, the house was unlocked, Bruce's van parked at the curb, though he'd told her (had he?) that he was scheduled to work.

Once again, she'd gotten her wires crossed.

She went in through the front door and headed straight for the kitchen, where a strange woman sat at the table, eating a meatball sandwich.

I'm in the wrong house, Dolly thought.

The woman stood. She was very tall, her blond hair teased into a little pouf. She looked as stunned as Dolly felt. "Ma, for God's sake! What are you doing here?"

For one terrible moment Dolly felt the room spin. Alzheimer's, she thought. Like poor Ida Binder, she was losing her mind.

She said, "I forgot my pills."

The strange woman took her arm. "You look flushed. Sit down, hon." Dolly did.

If she'd had her wits about her, she might have asked more questions. Instead, she held tightly to Bruce's hand. She drank a glass of water and swallowed the two pills he gave her, her heart still fluttering. And when she finally spoke, it was her heart talking:

"It's all right, dear. I don't mind."

Zoe lands on a Tuesday. Bruce and Dolly, ten minutes early, consult the monitors and follow the signs to Baggage Claim. In the long corridor, Dolly catches their reflection in the plate glass window: the big shambling man in a ball cap, the frail old lady in a canary-yellow suit. More and more, Bruce looks strange to her in male clothing, dressed in some elaborate disguise. Less frequently, she feels a tender pang of recognition. In his sloppy sweatshirts he could be the older brother—the father, even—of the sullen boy he used to be.

Last night he had lingered at the piano, playing a number of Dolly's favorites. Afterward, unusually, they watched the late news together, and she mixed them each a second drink.

The terminal seems busy for a weekday. A crowd mills around the conveyor belt: a sunburned family in flip-flops; several impatient men in suits; two baby-faced soldiers in desert camouflage; a woman shouting Spanish into a cell phone. Where, Dolly wonders, is everyone going? Years ago, people stayed put: you found a job and kept it, bought a house and kept it. There were meals to cook and children to raise, and in this way, years passed. Those who did otherwise—the unsavory characters, the criminals and misfits—were easy to spot, back when men got regular haircuts and shaved daily. Now they seem to be everywhere.

She picks out several dark-haired young women traveling alone, any one of whom might be Zoe—who, she now realizes, likely won't recognize them either. They met just once before, six years ago at Andrew's wedding. Too old to be a flower girl, Zoe was something called a junior bridesmaid, a chubby little thing in a puffy lavender dress.

"Uncle Bruce?"

They turn to see a big sturdy girl, nearly Bruce's height, though slightly stooped under the weight of a massive canvas rucksack. She wears a tattered denim jacket and rumpled pants with many pockets and, incredibly, a tiny silver ring in one nostril. Her hair is dyed red and cut into very short bangs, giving her a monkeyish look. Despite having received, in each year's Christmas card, a wallet-size school picture, Dolly would never have recognized her.

"Welcome to Baltimore," Bruce mumbles.

There is a moment of confusion in which Bruce offers his hand and Zoe leans in for a kiss. They end up doing both, awkwardly. Zoe's hand is covered with what looks like a bad case of psoriasis.

"Oh, dear," says Dolly. "What happened to your hand?"

Zoe holds out the hand, spreading her thick fingers. Dolly sees, then, that it is covered with an intricate design in red ink.

"Mehndi," says Zoe. "It's sort of a temporary tattoo. In India brides get them for their wedding day."

Heartened by the word *temporary*, Dolly rises on tiptoe to kiss her cheek.

Bruce plucks Zoe's bags from the carousel, two hefty suitcases with wheels on the bottom. Together with the rucksack, it seems like a lot of luggage for a seven-week visit.

At home, while Bruce carries the suitcases up to Andrew's old room and Dolly fries chicken for dinner, she hears, from the living room, a shriek of pain or delight. She finds Zoe standing in front of the piano, her shoulders shaking with laughter, a framed photo in her hand. "God, is this Andrew?"

He was a handsome man and had been a darling little boy but not, in truth, an attractive teenager. His high-school graduation portrait featured an unfortunate haircut with a sort of tail in back—the style in those days, apparently, though it's hard to imagine this ever seemed a good idea.

"What a tool," Zoe says.

This from a girl with a ring in her nose!

At dinner she takes second helpings of chicken and coleslaw. "This is *so good*," she says with her mouth full. The food at rehab is disgusting. Still, somehow, she gained six pounds.

Afterward, she excuses herself, leaving Dolly with the dishes. Bruce and Dolly watch "Jeopardy!" ignoring the overhead noises: the thumping bass of Zoe's radio, the unzipping of suitcases, the closing of bureau drawers.

This week's contestants are college students playing for charity. In his jeans and sweatshirt Bruce reverts to his teenage self, sprawled morosely on the divan.

If she'd had her wits about her, she'd have asked more questions.

Are you happy? Are you lonely? Is it my fault?

She had married young, as people used to. Her knowledge of men was gleaned from the movies. Of the available boys, she chose the handsomest, as the movies taught you to do. It took her years to understand that men and women were not the ideal companions for each other, the great, painful lesson of her long marriage: the sexes were simply too different, the distance between them too great.

Her whole married life she pined for her mother, her sisters. During both pregnancies she prayed for a daughter, a fact that haunts her now.

Just once—years ago, when Tony was still living—Bruce brought a girl home for dinner. His route then was in Catonsville, where he shared a rundown house with a revolving cast of roommates. Veronica was one of them, a hunched, skinny thing with crooked teeth and massive quantities of curly blond hair. The hair, her one attractive feature, was impossible to miss, since she fiddled with it constantly—even at the table, which was unsanitary (though perhaps Dolly shouldn't have said so). Over the years, Andrew would bring home a string of girlfriends, and Dolly would get more comfortable with the idea; but at the time, she'd been flummoxed by Bruce's attention to Veronica, the clumsy way he fell all over himself to pull out her chair. If she'd had a daughter of her own, Dolly might have taken it in stride, her home invaded by this ill-mannered young person. But she had been, always, the only lady in the house.

Women are not always kind to each other.

I'll do better next time, she told herself afterward. But there had been no next time.

"I'm sorry, dear," she told Bruce one night during "Jeopardy!" "I should have been nicer to your friend Veronica."

Bruce looked confused. He wore, that night, a cocktail dress in slimming black. "Veronica *Hamlin?*"

"I suppose so." Shamefully, she'd never bothered to learn the girl's last name.

There was a long silence in which Dolly invented an entirely different life for her son. She imagined a crowd at Christmas, a chorus of curly-haired grandchildren around her dinner table. Quietly, she sipped her drink, mixed with Fresca, since Bruce was on a diet.

When he finally spoke, it was to the television: "What is sublimation?"

At the commercial break, he took her hand. His was very soft, well moisturized. "She wasn't important, hon. I just liked her hair."

The next day, a Wednesday, Zoe registers for classes. Dolly takes the bus to her hair appointment, grateful for her familiar routine. Afterward, she stops at Pine Grove. The afternoon is balmy. She and Ida Binder walk arm in arm around the garden.

"Seven weeks is a long time," says Dolly. "I'm worried about Bruce."

Ida eyes her vacantly. In recent months her words have dried up, though occasionally her eyes seem full of something: Sympathy? Understanding? It's hard to say.

"Who's it hurting?" Dolly demands. "He isn't hurting anybody."

Ida does not disagree.

"It makes him happy. Nothing else ever has." As she says it, Dolly knows that this is true.

When she comes home from Pine Grove, she hears voices upstairs. She finds Bruce leaning in the doorway of Andrew's room. Zoe sits on the bed next to a heap of clothing, as though her two large suitcases have been turned upside down and emptied there.

"Carbs are the enemy," Bruce is saying as Dolly climbs the stairs.

At five o'clock Dolly starts dinner. She has defrosted three filets of flounder and is dredging them in breadcrumbs when Zoe appears in the kitchen. "Can I help?"

The answer, it turns out, is *no*: Zoe has no kitchen skills whatsoever. Her only proficiency involves opening cans. At rehab, she explains, the menu never varies: chili on Monday, taco salad on Tuesday; though it's really all the same meal, different combinations of corn chips, ground meat, tomatoes, and cheese. The tomatoes come from giant industrial-size cans; Zoe has seen them. Each client has kitchen duty one week a month.

"I didn't mind it," she says, shrugging. "It was, you know, something to do."

"Well, that's good." Dolly gropes for something more to say, but this proves unnecessary. Zoe, clearly, is a girl accustomed to an audience. She can hold a conversation all by herself.

"They were pretty good at keeping us busy. Every day, you had individual counseling, then art therapy, then yoga. Every night after dinner, we did sharing circles, and then Group."

When Dolly shows her how to set the table—forks to the left of the plate, knives to the right—she seems a little dazzled. The podiatrist, apparently, serves dinner cafeteria style, each family member filling his own plate from a pot on the stove. Dolly refrains from asking what sort of woman Andrew has married. Chastened by the memory of Veronica Hamlin, she keeps her opinion to herself.

She and Zoe are folding the napkins—the podiatrist uses paper ones—when Bruce clomps down the stairs in a flowered sundress. For a moment Dolly feels dizzy.

"I knew it would fit!" Zoe says.

"She's a sweet girl. The sweetest," Dolly tells Ida Binder. (Though the nose ring still throws her.)

The truth is that she does mind, a little. She minds all sorts of things. But minding is lonelier and harder, and where does it get you? People are in a hurry, and don't listen. They love you in between the dog track and the beer garden, after baseball season when there's nothing on TV. They forget to say thank you, to call or visit; they slouch at the table and play with their hair. Barbara Jean has made allowances. On the eve of her eightieth birthday, it's far too late to stop.

RICK HILLES

To the Language Spoken in the Country of Urgency

In the country of urgency, there is a language.
—*Grace Schulman*

I must have said something
to the man in my confusion

when I put my hand on his
shoulder long enough for

a cement truck to breeze by
—it would have killed him—

instantly, I think, when the light
changes and its change falls

through our long shadows,
spreading the news of sunset

over our faces and the wet streets
and we—the temporary single

organism of crowd—begin again
to cross the street, when the man

turns to face me now and asks
if I know Arabic. (I say, *I wish!*)

"Because just then it sounded
a lot like you were calling me

by name in the language of
my other mother country!"

ROBERT HELLENGA

A Christmas Letter

I was in Florence, Italy, when my father died. It was Easter Sunday and I was staying with old friends, the Marchettis, in their apartment near Piazza delle Cure, a quiet neighborhood on the north edge of town that you entered from via Faentina. We hadn't gone into the center for the big Easter celebration, but we'd watched the dove and the exploding cart on the television.

We were just sitting down to our first course—a rich broth thickened with egg yolks—when I got a telephone call from my sister. My sister doesn't speak Italian, but she managed to make herself understood, and Signora Marchetti waved me to the phone in the small entrance hallway.

"Are you ready for this?" my sister said.

"I'm ready."

"Dad's dead," she said. "Out at the club. He fell down in the locker room. Drunk. They couldn't rouse him. He was dead by the time they got him to the hospital."

"I thought they kicked him out of the club?"

"He got reinstated. He got a lawyer and threatened to sue them."

My father had taken up golf late in life. He was a natural athlete and was soon competing with the club champion. After my mother's death, he bought a small Airstream trailer and rented space on a lot across the road from the club entrance so he wouldn't have to drive home at night if he stayed late at the bar, which he often did.

"Where are you now?" I asked.

"I went out to the trailer earlier, just to have a look, but I'm at the house now. Dad's house."

"It must be pretty early."

"Seven o'clock," she said.

I pictured my sister, Gracie, in the breakfast nook of the kitchen we'd grown up in, in a lovely Dutch Colonial house about a mile north of town—a house that my father had built himself with help from *his* father. I pictured her sitting on the built-in blue bench at the built-in blue table, the cord from the phone on the wall stretched over her shoulder.

"What are you doing?" I asked.

"Just sitting here."

"How are you?"

"I'm fine, in fact. How about you?"

"I'm fine too."

"Have you met up with your friend yet?"

I'd come to Florence ostensibly to borrow one of Galileo's telescopes for the Galileo exhibit at the Museum of Science and Industry in Chicago, where I was employed as an exhibit developer. But really I'd come to see a woman with whom I was madly in love, a Scottish Italian fresco restorer, Rosella Douglas, who was working on the frescoes in the apse of Santa Croce.

I looked up at the Marchettis eating their soup at the long table in what was a combined kitchen–living room–dining room. Was someone listening to me? Luca was the only one who understood English, but he was seated at the far end of the table next to his grandmother.

"She's skiing in the Dolomites," I said. "She'll be back tomorrow night. I'm going to meet her at the station. Have you called people yet?"

"I'm going to do that today."

"Do you want me to come home?"

She laughed.

"What about the funeral?"

"His body went to the junior college. They did the removal last night. They've started a mortuary science program. They'll cremate what's left…send us the ashes."

"Dad was full of surprises, wasn't he?"

"We'll have to have some kind of memorial service when you get back. Maybe out at the cemetery."

My sister and I had been looking forward to this moment, but we hadn't really planned ahead. "Whatever you want to do will be fine," I said. "You're the one who's had to put up with him."

"Sometimes I think I should have moved away, like you did. But then I met Pete, and that was that. No way Pete was going to leave Green Arbor." Though they were divorced now, and Pete had, in fact, left Green Arbor. Probably to get away from my father, who had treated him like an errand boy.

There were sixteen of us at the long table. Signora Marchetti (Claudia) had kept a bowl of soup warm for me. Chiara, who was my age, forty, put it on the table in front of me and stood for a moment with her hand on my shoulder. I'd spent a year at the Marchettis as an exchange student when I was in high school, and then again when I came back to Florence on a study-abroad program, and then at various other times over the years. Chiara was like a second sister, and Luca like a younger brother. I got on well with all of them and with their cousins and aunts and uncles and with the grandmother, Nonna Agostina, who was seated in the place of honor at the head of the table.

Faces turned toward me as I took my place at the opposite end of the table from Nonna Agostina.

"My sister," I said. "Calling to wish me a happy Easter."

I had to make a conscious effort to suppress my relief, my sudden joy, though, in fact, it was more complicated than that. I was glad that my father was dead, but I wasn't glad that I was glad. I would have preferred to be grief-stricken. And I was saddened by the sharp contrast between my own little family—Gracie, Dad, and me—with the extended family—four generations—passing their empty plates to Chiara and Luca, who were helping their mother and father clear the table. But the soup was delicious, and so was the roast baby lamb. Sensation is sensation.

When I first heard of the Oedipus complex at the University of Michigan—we were reading *Oedipus* in a "Great Books" course—I knew exactly what Freud was talking about. Dad had become more and more abusive toward my mother, who suffered from tic douloureux. She was a lovely woman, small in stature, but big-hearted, generous spirited, deeply religious. She played the organ and directed the choir at the Methodist church. *You just married me for the money,* he'd say to her. Drunk. *For a free ride.* It would have been a blessing if he'd died first. She could have lived out her last years in peace instead of in a nightmare.

And where was I? I'd run away. To Ann Arbor. And then Chicago. It was my sister who bore the brunt of my father's anger during the last years of my mother's life, and beyond. I was afraid of my father—most people were—and my only attempt to intervene was a disaster: It's Christmas Eve. I'm a wise fool, just home from Ann Arbor for Christmas vacation. My sister has taken Mom out on a last-minute shopping trip. They're not home by five o'clock and Dad is working himself up into a rage. Every fifteen minutes or so he goes out to his gun room at the back of the garage for a nip of Jack Daniels, which he has to do because drinking is not allowed in our house. "I try to be a good husband..." he says, over and over. "I do everything I can..." "And now look at this..." He shrugs helplessly. "She'll be overtired." He's indulging in his favorite fantasy, which is that everything he does is for my mother's sake. He calls me in Ann Arbor, for example, on Sunday mornings. If I'm at home, in my dorm room in Adams House in the West Quad, which I usually am, he'll want to know why I'm not in church. "Your mother wants you to go to church...And you'll go. Next Sunday you'll attend the Methodist church or I'll come up there and find out the reason why."

It's late when my mother and sister get home—after six o'clock. They've had a wonderful time, but Dad blows a gasket, is in a towering rage. I can hear him chewing out my mother in the bedroom. "You know better than to get overtired...I try to be a good husband, I try to do the best I can, and now look at you. You've been gone for four hours...You've tired yourself out. You know better..." And so on.

The bedroom door is not locked. Mom is sitting on the bed. Dad is shouting at her, repeating himself. "What were you thinking?... How could you?...I do everything I can...I try to be a good husband, but..."

"Leave her alone," I say. "She had a good time. Why do you have to ruin it?"

Dad gives me a look of contempt. "Get out."

"Leave her alone," I say. "You're too drunk to know what you're doing."

This is the Oedipal moment. I would kill him if I dared, if I could.

He's a big man. Drunk. "Like a raging bull elephant in musth," as my sister and I sometimes say to each other later.

He slaps me so hard I fall down.

My mother is crying.

I get up and he slaps me again, backhanded, on the other side of my face.

I run out of the room.

And that's a story I've never told to anyone before, but one I've had to live with for years. I've never been able to forget, or to forgive. But there's more.

Later on—Dad asleep in his chair—we do the usual. My sister and her husband, Pete, and their daughter, Megan, are there. Mom reads the Christmas story from the Gospel of Luke. We've decorated the tree, and there's a fire in the fireplace. We don't talk about what happened. Maybe that silence is the greater act of cowardice. Megan, age twelve, is the only one who stands up to my father. When she was little, he would force her to eat sweet potatoes or candied carrots, which she couldn't stand, and he'd make a big battle out of it. She'd eat the sweet potatoes or candied carrots or whatever it was and then throw up on the table. Finally, he gave up. But he respected her. At least he left her alone.

Later on, in the middle of the night, I can hear him typing. He's retired early—too early—in order to spend more time hunting and fishing. He's turned his wholesale lumber business, which specialized in choice hardwoods—cherry from western Pennsylvania and West Virginia, yellow poplar from Appalachia, yellow birch from Canada, black walnut from Indiana—over to some of his key employees, who have embezzled so much money that the company has fallen into the hands of the receivers, a phrase that my father repeats over and over: *fallen into the hands of the receivers.* He wants to go back into business and repay the creditors, firms he'd done business with over the years. But the credit rating agency won't give him back his old credit rating, and without his credit rating, he can't, or won't, go back into business, and that's what the letter is about—addressed not to the men who defrauded him, but to the credit rating bureau. He's been working on it—sending it out, demanding meetings, switching lawyers—for six or seven years, working on it day and night, including Christmas Eve. On Christmas morning we go over the letter again. It's the same letter every year. It's a good thing he doesn't have a computer, because then he wouldn't have to retype it, and the typing is a kind of therapy for him. He types so hard he ruins two or three Underwood office typewriters a year.

In any case, we go over the letter as if nothing had happened the night before. I advise him to go easy on the capital letters, and he agrees. He retypes the letter, jabbing at the keys with two thick fingers, a job that takes him about twenty minutes. I look it over again. There are a couple of typos. He retypes it again, and then again. Pretty soon all the adjectives and verbs are recapitalized. For emphasis. "Although I am neither RICH nor POWERFUL, nonetheless if you THINK..."

Then the nouns and adverbs. And then every word: "ALTHOUGH I AM NEITHER RICH NOR POWERFUL, NONETHELESS, IF YOU THINK..."

On Easter evening at the Marchettis, after most of the relatives, including Nonna Agostina, had gone home, I played a beautiful mahogany guitar that Luca, a professional musician, got in Paris the year before. I knew a handful of Italian songs and we sang "Bella Ciao" and "Il Cacciatore Gaetano." It was a twelve-fret classical guitar with a wide neck and short scale, very easy to play. I tuned it down to an open G and played a new version of "Corrina, Corrina" that I'd found on YouTube, on an Italian site, actually. The song articulated the kind of melancholy I often experience after a few glasses of wine, and I was moved to open my heart to the Marchettis. I did not, however, tell them that my father had died drunk in the locker room of the Green Arbor Country Club. I just said how moved I was to see four generations together with the grandmother at the head of the table. Four generations.

And then the truth came out with a bang: No one could stand the grandmother, Signora Marchetti's mother. Signora Marchetti had one brother and two sisters, and they moved Nonna Agostina around from house to house. But she kept her old *casa* near Palazzo Strozzi, even though she went back to it only once a year. She was tight with money. She was always changing her will to punish her children, usually the son or daughter she was living with. Everyone hated her. Even the grandchildren.

I was floored. It was like discovering that there's no Santa Claus—or no Easter Bunny. It was worse than that. It was like discovering...I didn't know what it was like discovering. I still don't.

Rosella—the woman I was in love with—was going to take the CIT bus from Cortina d'Ampezzo, where she'd been skiing with her *friend* and his children, to Venice, and then a Eurostar to Florence. I drank a coffee in the station bar, checked the schedule, and then waited for her on a bench at the end of track 6. We'd met at a party in Hyde Park (Chicago, not London) to which I'd been invited because I spoke Italian, which turned out not to be necessary. "We'll speak Italian when you come to Italy," she said. "But in the United States we'll speak English." Her mother was from the Orkney Islands and her father was Italian.

She spoke English fluently, but with a pronounced Scottish accent. She didn't say "wee" and "bonny," but she rolled her r's and collapsed her words into as few syllables as possible, and the first time we made love she said, "Whun ye feel it coomin, luv, tock it oot," because she suddenly remembered that she'd forgotten to take her birth-control pill. I took it out, spilled my seed on the bed, and she laughed and drew me down to her. She tasted sweet and salty.

She'd come to Chicago for a conference on fresco restoration. I took some time off and went to a couple of her lectures at the Art Institute, and one at the Newberry Library, and I showed her the main sights, including some of the exhibits I'd worked on at the Museum of Science and Industry: "The History of Computers," "Life Tech," "Blue Planet, Red Planet." She'd spent time in California and New York, but it was her first time in Chicago, and she expected to find an old bluesman on every street corner, but she had to settle for Roy Book Binder at the Old Town School and Cephas & Wiggins at Buddy Guy's, and all the time, I was thinking that what we were doing was having a little adventure, *una piccola avventura.* But by the time I dropped her off at O'Hare— she was on her way to New York—she had become the person in whose eyes I wanted to shine, and I gave her a Galilean-style telescope kit I'd created for the Galileo exhibit out of a cardboard mailing tube and a pair of lenses. It was two feet long and we managed to squeeze it into her suitcase at the last minute.

She wasn't married, and neither was I, but she was somebody's mistress and lived in a house on this somebody's estate on the side of Monte Ceceri, above Fiesole. "It's one of those complicated European affairs," she said. "You Americans, you Middle-of-the-Westerners, wouldn't understand." She laughed. I was standing with her in the check-in line in the United Terminal.

"I understand all right," I said. "You've got yourself a sugar daddy in Fiesole, and he cheats on his wife and now you're cheating on him."

"*Sugarrr daddy.*" She growled. "That's exactly what I told you: you don't understand a thing."

Sitting by the tracks in the station in Florence, I could close my eyes and still hear her laughter over the sound of the trains. Love made the world bigger, louder, more surprising, brought what was blurry into sharp focus. But what about my parents? What had happened? What had gone wrong? Would things have been better if my mother had allowed my father to drink in the house? That was one theory, my ex-brother-in-law's theory, and it made a certain amount of sense. But it was a theory I didn't want to pursue. But going back even further. I could remember the first time I heard them quarreling. Adults didn't quarrel in Green Arbor, Michigan. Not when I was growing up, and that's why it made such an impression on me. I woke up in the night. My mother wasn't saying anything, but my father was shouting something about the new mantel over the fireplace in the living room. "God damn it," he shouted, "if you didn't want it that way, you should have said so." I couldn't hear my mother, and I never figured out what the problem was with the mantel.

At the University of Michigan I majored in philosophy. I read Thomas Kuhn and Karl Popper and specialized in philosophy of science, which is how I wound up in Chicago at the Museum of Science and Industry as an exhibit developer. On Tuesday I was going to ask the director of the Museo di Storia della Scienza in Florence if I could borrow Galileo's telescope for the Galileo exhibit at MSI. It was out of the question, I'd told my boss. The famous telescope that Galileo used for his observations for *Sidereus Nuncius* was going to the Franklin Institute in Philadelphia. But there was a second telescope, a smaller prototype that we were aiming at. It had a magnification of 14x, as opposed to 20x, and a focal length of 1330mm with a 26mm aperture.

I was thinking about this second telescope—comparing it in my mind to the telescope kit I'd put together for the exhibit—when Rosella came up behind me and put her arms around me. "*Sorpreso?*"

"*Stupito,*" I said. Amazed. I really was amazed. Amazed to be taken by surprise like that, and to hear Italian instead of Scots coming out of her mouth.

We backed up a little, looked each other up and down, and stepped into each other's embrace. The train, which had backed into the station, was already pulling out, on its way to Rome. We walked to the new parking lot, and I hoisted her big suitcase into the trunk of a smallish Alfa Romeo.

"Is this a Spider?" I asked. It was the only kind of Alfa Romeo I could name.

"A Brera," she said. "It's small, but not too small. I couldn't fit this suitcase into a Spider. Would you like to drive it?"

I declined automatically. I'd never driven in Italy and had no desire to. But then all of a sudden it hit me: I could buy a car like this. I could buy two of them. I could buy anything I wanted. Now that my father was dead, I was rich.

"*Momento*," I said. "Maybe I will drive."

I hadn't been to bed with a woman since Rosella's two-week stay in Chicago, the previous October, and I didn't want to disturb the prospect of bliss by telling her about my father's death. In my mind, what had started as a *piccola avventura,* with a predictable trajectory, had turned into the real thing. Even before she left Chicago. But what was the "real thing"? And how would it turn out? On the one hand, I wanted to deromanticize it. We were both adults, after all. This wasn't a teenage infatuation. On the other hand…But you can't think about these things when you're driving in Italy. Rosella guided me through a complex maze of streets in which you have to go south in order to go north, east in order to go west, until finally we were on the familiar bus route up to Fiesole, and then through the piazza in Fiesole and on up Monte Ceceri and down a narrow wooded lane that was like a tunnel, green as dark as midnight, till we came to a big wooden door in a stone wall. It was thrilling. Rosella got out, opened the door, I drove through, and she closed the door and got back into the car. It was like a fairy tale; and the house, her house, the house provided for her by her sugar daddy, was like a glass palace. Like the Philip Johnson glass house in New Canaan, Connecticut.

"I'm the one who suggested the glass," she said. "So now he said I have to live here. I used to live closer to the villa. Further down the road." The road disappeared into the darkness.

"Well, you're pretty isolated," I said.

"We can pull the drapes," she said. "If you're self-conscious."

Maybe I *was* self-conscious, but I didn't say so.

"Let's go to bed right away," she said, once we got into the house. "Then we can enjoy our dinner later. Besides, it's chilly in here. That will give it a chance to warm up." She adjusted the thermostat. "We can talk later. You can tell me all about Galileo. His tomb's in Santa Croce, you know."

"Yes," I said. "I'm going to see if we can borrow it for the MSI exhibit."

"The tomb?" Then she laughed. She had pinned her hair back, and in the bedroom, she stood in front of a mirror and combed it out. Hurry up and wait. She was making me wait, but I didn't mind. I studied an etching on the wall signed Rembrandt van Rijn: a young couple making love.

"Is this real? I ask. I mean really a Rembrandt?"

"Yes, but it's not mine. It comes with the house."

"The woman has three hands."

"He forgot to erase one when he changed the position. But look at the smile on her face."

It was a lovely smile, a wonderful smile, like the smile on the face of a young woman I'd been watching over and over on a YouTube video—a slide-guitar version of "Corrina, Corrina."

I watched Rosella's shadow moving on the wall as she took her clothes off. When she turned toward me and smiled a smile that spread through her whole body, I could see tiny creases under her eyes. She was irresistible. But over her shoulder, in the mirror, I could see something moving outside the bedroom window, something at the edge of the darkness. The drapes had not been pulled. I turned to look. It was an enormous white pig, coming closer, walking stiff-legged. She came right up to the glass wall and pressed her nose up against it. For a moment I thought I was coming unstrung, but Rosella put her hand on my back, as if to steady me.

"It's Elena," she said. "She's supposed to be penned in up at the villa, but sometimes she gets loose. She's attracted to the light. They have quite a few animals."

"*They?*"

"The family."

"She's huge."

"Over two hundred fifty kilos. Do you want me to chase her away?"

"No, no," I said. "It's all right."

"She'll wander off when I turn out the light."

After we had made love, Rosella cooked spaghetti with garlic and oil, the simplest meal in the world, and one of the most satisfying. No salad—the shops were closed on Easter Monday evening. There was nothing else to eat in the house except some crackers and a bowl of apples, big Granny Smiths, past their prime. We each ate an apple, using knives and forks.

After supper, we went outside and looked at the night sky through the crude cardboard telescope I'd given Rosella. No sign of Elena. The moon was full, but due to the small field of vision inherent in the design, you could see only half of it at a time.

"Before Galileo," I said, "astronomers thought that the sky had been completely explored. Everything—all the planets, all the fixed stars—had been cataloged. There was nothing more to discover. Who would have thought that by sticking two eyeglass lenses into the ends of a tube..."

"They had eyeglasses?"

"Eyeglasses were invented in the late Middle Ages," I said. "That's what you've got in this tube, more or less. Sixteen dollars for a pair of lenses, thirty-five dollars for the whole kit."

We looked at the North Star and at Vega, which was rising in the northeast, and at Jupiter, though the telescope wasn't powerful enough to pick out the moons, and then we went back inside and looked through Rosella's computer at a DVD with close-up photos—a slide show—of Rosella's own work between the Gothic ribs at the top of the apse of Santa Croce—the Cappella Maggiore. We looked at hands and feet and robes and faces that had been cleaned, and the tips of an angel's wings, the feathers newly restored to their original luster.

"Fresco restoration is a craft," she said. "You have to be an artisan, to work with your hands without leaving a mark. And at the same time, you have to be an artist, to use your imagination, and you've got to be a scientist too, a chemist; you've got to know how to inject polyvinylacetate resin into areas where the plaster surface is in danger of separating and breaking. You've got to know how to apply a solution of dimethylformamide to salt efflorescences of calcium carbonate. You've got to know how to apply diluted acrylic resin to consolidate pigments that are not adhering well. And you've got to be an historian, your job is to hang onto things that are passing away, disintegrating, your job is to preserve the old visual culture. Now we're in a new visual culture. It's impoverished in some ways, but rich in others. The problem is that people don't know how to understand the symbols, how to read them critically."

"OK," I said. "You don't have to be so defensive. I get your point. Is this a speech you give to tourists?"

"Something I go over in my own mind to convince myself that what I'm doing is important." She stopped and smiled. "I tend to get carried away. You'll have to come up on the scaffolding with me, then you'll understand."

Scaffolding? the top of a Gothic cathedral? I was picturing Juliette Binoche in *The English Patient,* hoisted up to the top of a church so she can examine the frescoes. No thanks. But I didn't want Rosella to know that I was afraid of heights. I wasn't cripplingly acrophobic, but I never stood close to the floor-to-ceiling windows in a high rise, and I never took the glass elevators in Water Tower Place.

"You'll have to wear a hard hat," she said, too interested in the slide show to notice my lack of enthusiasm, interested in the frescoes not so much as works of art, but as things, physical objects, subject to decay in a way that a poem or a piece of music is not. "When they're covered on the outside," she said, "with an accumulation of dirt and grime and candle smoke, you can clean them. When they're threatened from the inside by corrosive salts erupting from within the very stones of the cathedral, you can dissolve the salts. But when they're gone, like half the Giotto frescoes in the Peruzzi Chapel, they're gone forever."

When the slide show was over, I sat down at the computer and Googled the YouTube site on the Internet, the one with the smiling woman. It's an Italian site and the men you see at the opening are Italian, and the man wearing headphones says something in Italian—too fast for me—and counts down in Italian. The voice of the singer sounds like an old black man from the Delta, but the video doesn't match the audio. The young man playing a guitar in the video is strumming away wildly with a flatpick, but what you hear on the audio track is someone fingerpicking a slow blues: *Corrina, Corrina, where you been so long?* And then, during the second and third verses, you see the young man and this lovely woman sitting together. Talking. She turns to him and smiles.

"Look at her smile," I said. "It's like the smile in the etching."

Rosella looked at me, astonished. "That's Joan Baez," she said. "And Bob Dylan."

"Really? It doesn't say that on the website."

"*Porcamadonna!* How could you not recognize Joan Baez and Bob Dylan? You're kidding me?"

"No, I had no idea."

"Well," she said, "they're very young."

"That's not Bob Dylan singing, is it?"

She shook her head. "I don't think so."

"He can do gravelly," I said. "And he's the one who made that song popular."

We went back to bed. Rosella left the light on. She couldn't stop smiling. "I can't believe you didn't recognize Joan Baez and Bob Dylan." And she—Rosella—seemed to have three hands, like the woman in the etching, all pinching, tickling, massaging, scratching, poking.

Afterward she fell asleep, but I was wide awake. I propped myself up on one elbow and watched her for a while, and then I got up and went outside. I slipped on my leather jacket, which I'd bought at a discount store in Chicago, and put an apple in one of the side pockets. I turned the porch light on. A bicycle was leaning against the side of the house, and I was tempted to go for a spin. The road, or lane, led back down to Fiesole or up to the villa. But it was too dark to see, and the house was too isolated. Low streaky clouds had covered the moon. There was almost no light except the light from the house itself, the porch light, and a lamp on the table next to the bed, which I'd left on. I could see into the bedroom. Rosella had covered herself with a sheet.

I walked out to the edge of the darkness, out of sight of the house. I could sense trees, but I couldn't tell what kind they were. Maybe olive trees. I felt a branch but couldn't find any olives. It was too early anyway. It wasn't cold, but it was chilly, and after a few minutes I was ready to go back inside. But I'd forgotten about Elena. Two hundred fifty kilos. A third of a ton. Pure white, like the moon. She was standing under the light, between me and the door. I walked around the house. There's another door that opens into the kitchen. But it was locked. I knew enough about pigs not to challenge her. I'd helped my girlfriend's father rustle hogs a couple of times when I was in high school, and what I knew was that if a farmer had a heart attack in his field, the pigs would eat him.

I took the apple out of my jacket pocket and held it out to her. "Elena," I said. "How about a nice Granny Smith?" She really was enormous.

"Elena, Elena, *vieni mi qua,* come and get this nice apple." I took a bite out of the apple. She moved her head, and I could see she was tempted. It took about five minutes to lure her away from the front door. She moved toward me in her stiff-legged gait. Closer and closer. She seemed interested, rather than hostile, as if she were interrogating me. I thought about throwing the apple down on the ground, but decided against it. I held it in the palm of my hand as she came closer. She knocked it out of my hand with her snout, waited for my reaction, then picked it up with her mouth. I walked around her, slowly, on my way to the door, trailing my fingertips over her back, which looked furry but felt scratchy as sand paper.

She raised her head, looking for another apple. I went inside, brought out the bowl of apples, and fed them to her one at a time till they were all gone. And then I got back into bed with Rosella.

On Tuesday morning, I met with the director of the Museo di Storia della Scienza, who was pleased that I spoke Italian. He didn't make any promises about the second telescope, but he sent me to the Fondazione Scienza e Tecnica in via Giusti, near the Protestant Cemetery, where I spent a pleasant afternoon, though our own collection at MSI already contained most of the sixteenth-century astronomical and mathematical instruments that we needed for the exhibit.

On my way to Piazza Santa Croce to meet Rosella, I stopped and browsed the windows of several real estate agencies. I liked the looks of a two-bedroom apartment on Borgo Pinti for €600.000. It would be perfect. Rosella could walk to work. The words of the notice embedded themselves in my brain: *LUMINOSO appartamento*. It was on the *piano nobile* of an old palazzo that had been recently restored. Large living room. Modern kitchen. Two bedrooms. Two baths. Rooftop terrace. I was feeling optimistic that evening as the waiter at the Osteria dei Pazzi, who knew Rosella by name, seated us at a table by the window. But Rosella was preoccupied because, out of the blue, the Italian government had decided that it needed to exercise more control over restorers. The first step was a decree that all restorers would have to have a university degree.

"All of a sudden twenty thousand restorers aren't restorers," she kept saying. "This country is impossible. You can't live here." She tore off a chunk of *pane toscano* and put it in her mouth. "And this bread is ridiculous. Everywhere else in the whole world they know enough to put salt in their bread. The Florentines are the only people in the whole world who don't know this. What is the matter with these people? It's insane."

"That's because their food is so salty already."

"Instead of putting so much salt in the food, they should put some of it in the bread. Twenty thousand restorers won't be restorers if the Italian government has its way." She shook her head.

She ordered the *antipastone* for both of us. I understood that *antipastone* meant "big antipasto," but I didn't understand that it meant that the waiters would keep bringing us food till we couldn't possibly eat any more, not even one more olive: salami, prosciutto, cheeses, octopus salad, anchovies, roast vegetables, roast beef, *lardo di colonnata*—thin white slices of lard that have been specially cured in marble basins at Colonnata, near Carrara. But lard nonetheless, a Tuscan delicacy.

It was while we were eating straight lard that I proposed to Rosella. I didn't know what I'd do if she laughed in my face. My clothes, my suitcase, were at her house, so I couldn't have just walked out of the restaurant. I was trying to stay focused in the present moment, to detach myself from the result, to identify with the watcher watching myself rather than with my ego.

She didn't laugh, nor did she throw herself into my arms. She listened as if she were listening to a business proposition. The fact that we were in love was very important, but it was only one part of a larger picture.

She called to the head waiter, a man who burst into song every so often, and asked for another quarto of wine. It wasn't a fancy place. Comfortable. Not too expensive.

I told her about my father's death, though I didn't mention that he'd died on Easter Sunday, only four days ago, and she became tender and understanding. But, she said, she had her own situation to consider, the situation that was too complicated for an American to understand, the situation that involved a rich older man who had a life of his own— a wife, several children, old money, old aristocracy, a big estate with several houses, animals… She was right. I didn't understand.

"How would we live?" she wanted to know. "Fresco restorers don't make a lot of money. How would you find a job in Italy?"

I had, in fact, given this question some thought, but I didn't want to play my trump card, didn't want to tell her that now that my father was dead, I was a rich man too. I wanted her to meet me halfway.

"Museum jobs," she said, "any state jobs, are impossible to get. You'd have to enter a *concorso*, a competitive examination, along with hundreds of other people. And even if you won, which you wouldn't, because the exams are rigged—there's a lot of horse trading—you might be sent to Calabria."

"One of the American programs? There are forty-three of them in Florence."

"You wouldn't make enough money."

Our waiter had cleared the table and brought a bottle of *vin santo* and some *biscotti di Prato*. Rosella dipped a biscotto into her glass of wine.

"Rosella," I said. "I want this to matter. I want *us* to matter, you and I. I want us to be important. This isn't a little adventure."

"You never know what's important and what's not important till it's over, do you?"

On Wednesday and Thursday afternoons, around five o'clock, we met at the statue of Dante in Piazza Santa Croce and then took the No. 7 bus up to Fiesole, where she'd left her Alfa Romeo Brera parked near the Roman amphitheater. Sometimes she took the tunnel-like lane, sometimes a regular road that took us past the villa where her sugar daddy lived.

We made love first thing every evening, early, so we could enjoy our dinner later. Elena did not reappear, but we went up to visit her in her pen behind the villa. The signora was in Rome; the signore and his older son were still in the Dolomites, where the slopes were covered with snow year round.

"She's got a very low center of gravity," Rosella said as we admired the gigantic sow. "But she's very fast. If you want her to move forward, you have to enter her flight zone from behind the point of balance, which is right between her shoulders; and you have to remember, her field of vision is almost three hundred sixty degrees, so the only time she can't see you is if you're right behind her. If you want her to back up, you have to enter the flight zone from in front of the point of balance."

"You know a lot about pigs," I said.

"I know a lot about Elena," she said.

She'd borrowed a guitar from a fellow restorer so I could play for her. I tuned it down to an open G and played "Corrina, Corrina" while she cooked. I used a table knife as a slide.

"You know," she said. "I don't like the second verse of that song." She repeated the last line: "*ain't got Corrina, life don't mean a thing.*

I don't think you can look to another person for your salvation, to give meaning to your life."

"Then I won't sing it again," I said.

On Friday morning—we were going to have lunch later at the Osteria dei Pazzi—we met at Dante's cenotaph in the right aisle of the basilica. She wanted to take me up to the vault at the top of the apse, where she was working on the feet of St. Francis himself. The vault at the top of the apse was about the last place I wanted to be. The scaffolding was massive, not at all like the sort of thing painters put up at the side of a house. It filled the entire apse of Capella Maggiore. Even so, looking up into that airy dome—I counted nine levels or floors—made me a little bit seasick.

I had secured the second Galileo telescope, as well as an unusual astrolabe, so I wouldn't be going home empty-handed. There were still contracts to negotiate regarding the insurance, method of transportation, dates, and so on. I wouldn't be carrying the telescope, which looked like a piece of broom handle, back in my suitcase, of course, but I would finish up my part on Monday. The MSI lawyers would worry about the fine print. But I was not in a mood to congratulate myself, because I didn't know if I'd see Rosella again after today, didn't know if she'd be back from organizing a demonstration in Rome, didn't know what she'd decided, or what would be settled up in the apse, didn't know if whatever it was we were doing was important, or if it would turn out to be just a *piccola avventura,* didn't tell her about the luminoso apartment. Not yet anyway.

The elevator made me nervous, though it was huge, so we put on hard hats and took the stairs. Up nine stories, each floor supported by metal braces inserted into the holes in the wall that had been made when the church was built in the thirteenth century.

Rosella stopped to chat with someone on each level and to introduce me and to explain what was going on. You could see the joins where one day's work, or *giornata,* had overlapped another. In places, you could see traces of the preparatory drawing in *verdaccio,* a sort of second underdrawing that repeated and corrected the sinopia, or first underdrawing. You could see places where the pigment layer was flaking, and areas where the pigment itself had been weakened by the binding medium or by surface abrasion. She explained the properties of the different fixatives (organic and inorganic), emulsions, and solvents (volatile and polar) that were used to remedy these problems.

We stopped on the eighth level for a cup of coffee in a large office, the sort of office you might find in downtown Chicago—full of desks, waste baskets, lamps, a copy machine, a fax machine, telephones. And an espresso maker.

The apse had been frescoed by Agnolo Gaddi, who had learned from his more famous father, Taddeo, and from Giotto, but who had done something different, moving toward the international Gothic style. But the scaffolding makes it impossible to take in the big picture, "The History of the True Cross."

Rosella was working on the frescoes between the ribs of a vaulted arch at the very top of the apse. We were face to face with St. Francis, the four Evangelists, and the risen Christ, and we had to take off our hard hats so we wouldn't scrape the ceiling.

"Vaults need special treatment," she said, "because the undersurface is lath rather than stone.

"What about these big cracks?" I asked. "Are you going to seal them up?"

"No," she said. "If you fill them, that just redirects the stress. You smooth them out and seal the raw stone at the edges so it doesn't disintegrate any further."

I was so overwhelmed just by the idea of being up there that I forgot to be afraid. Overwhelmed and feeling very special, very much the insider. I even let Rosella walk me to the edge of the scaffolding so I could look down into the big barnlike nave. She put her hand on my back to steady me, as she had done when Elena first appeared at the glass wall of her bedroom.

Far below us groups of tourists followed guides holding bright umbrellas, stopping in front of the famous tombs: Dante's (empty), Machiavelli's, Michelangelo's, Galileo's, Rossini's. A service was being conducted in one of the smaller chapels directly below us. We couldn't see the priest, but we could see the people in an area that had been roped off. Everywhere you looked people were taking photos. Isolated worshippers were scattered here and there. In the right aisle, a mother and father consulted a guidebook while two children ran up and down the aisle. They had to make way for a mother and teenage daughter pushing an infant in a stroller. A workman rolled a cart of stuff to the elevator. Some women in blue aprons were polishing the altar railings. (The main altar had been relocated to make room for the scaffolding.) A priest hurried toward the sacristy—we couldn't see the entrance from the scaffolding. Two other priests, crossing paths in front of the pulpit, stopped to chat. A line snaked out in front of a confessional. Two young lovers held hands. Two middle-aged women held hands. A beggar sat on the pavement by the ticket booth. You couldn't just wander in anymore. You had to pay. A bridal party had gathered around the ticket booth and the bride was arguing with the woman who sold the tickets. Probably a wedding party on their way to the wedding hall in Palazzo Vecchio.

What had happened to the original Franciscan vows of poverty? Legend has it that one of the friars responsible for the construction of the elaborate basilica was now in Purgatory being struck on the head by two hammers continuously.

Rosella pointed out the line of the water from the big flood of 1966. The basilica—the whole Santa Croce district—was in the flood plain. The water had burst the huge doors.

I thought this view of the nave was what Rosella had wanted to show me. But I was wrong. What she wanted to show me was in a corner, in a small space at the base of one of the ribs, where the *intonaco* had been completely worn away. She pointed to a small oval portrait. A man in a floppy medieval hat, bright red—a jester? a peasant? a noble? a holy fool? I didn't recognize him at first. I was reading it as a late medieval portrait, and I was only semiliterate. It didn't make sense. I had to adjust my eyes. And then I recognized myself. It was me. This was her gift to me. At first I didn't understand. Then I did. And I understood that she was saying good-bye, that it was now too late to play my trump card, my ace in the hole. Too late to say I was rich, too late to tell her about the *appartamento LUMINOSO* on Borgo Pinti with the terrace on the roof.

"It's true a *fresco*," she said: "the lath, then the arriccio, the sinopia, the intonaco, the paint applied to the wet plaster. Then a few details a secco. Certain pigments you can't use in true fresco. It will be there for centuries. You can see St. Francis and the Evangelists."

"And they can see me," I said. "Can you do this?" I added. "I mean, can you get away with it?"

"I've already gotten away with it."

*

My sister and I spent the week before Christmas in the old family home surrounded by old familiar things—the bright blue table in the breakfast nook, the deep red davenport in the living room that was always threatening to collapse, my mother's walnut Steinway piano, the silverware and the plates we'd eaten off of as children, the glasses we'd drunk out of, Dad's typewriter on the desk in the little office off the front hall. A copy of the letter still curled up in the rollers. Two of the keys— the s and the t—were completely broken, but he'd kept typing anyway: ALHOUGH I AM NEIHER RICH NOR POWERFUL, NONEHELE, IF YOU HINK...

I had never gotten around to playing my trump card in Florence, and it was just as well, because my father left his estate, valued at about eight million dollars, to the Methodist church. Except for the house, which went to my sister, and the Airstream trailer, which went to me. The church already had a new roof and a new electronic organ. The brick walls had been tuck-pointed, and the pastor was living in a new parsonage. It wasn't Santa Croce, but it was something.

On Sunday, two days before Christmas, my sister and I went to the ceremony in which the new organ was dedicated to my mother. And afterward, we went out to the cemetery, just the two of us, and buried the urn that held Dad's ashes. The ground was frozen, but the hole, which had been dug months earlier, had been filled with straw. All we had to do was stick the urn in the ground. Someone from the cemetery would cover it with dirt and sod. But later.

We could have contested the will, but we didn't, and we didn't experience the rancor we might have felt. Eight million dollars. I could have bought the appartamento luminoso in Borgo Pinti. Gracie could have quit her job at the library and moved to the Florida Keys with her new boyfriend. Liberation, not rancor, was what we experienced. We were finally out from under. The money would have weighed us down. We were better off as we were. The Galileo exhibit was on schedule. Gracie had become the head librarian in Green Arbor. The library was planning to expand. We were almost festive at the cemetery.

On Christmas Eve we pan-fried a couple of small steaks and cooked some mushrooms and made a salad and drank most of a bottle of Bordeaux, and then we sat on the davenport in front of the fire in the living room and enjoyed the Christmas tree we'd decorated earlier. In the morning Gracie's boyfriend and his two kids were coming. We were going to cook a turkey and everything that goes with a turkey. Gracie had already baked the pies.

I'd sold the Airstream, and Gracie had put the house up for sale. We opened another bottle of wine and fought off the ghosts of Christmases past, though many of them were happy ones, and I told her about Rosella, told her the story I've told you: Easter dinner at the Marchettis, the Rembrandt etching of the woman with three hands, the huge sow pressing her nose against the glass wall and then knocking the big Granny Smith apple out of my hand with her snout, the YouTube video of Joan Baez and Bob Dylan, looking through the window at Rosella asleep, the lardo di colonnata in the Osteria dei Pazzi, drinking coffee in an office on the eighth floor of the scaffolding, removing my hard hat so it wouldn't scrape the ceiling in Santa Croce, Jesus and the Evangelists, looking down at the nave without fear—fear overwhelmed by beauty. And my picture. Painted in the true fresco manner. A gift from the heart.

"Did it matter?" I asked my sister. "Was it important? Did it matter? Does anything matter? You know what she said to me? Rosella?"

"What did she say?"

"She said 'you never know if something matters till it's over.' And now it's over, and I still don't know. What's the measure of change? Shouldn't something be different now? If she'd said yes, then it would have 'mattered' because it would have been a turning point in my life. Everything would be different. I'd be in Italy right now. You could be in Italy too. Or Florida. Down in the Keys."

"But she didn't say yes. And you couldn't have bought the luminoso apartment anyway, because you didn't inherit any money." Gracie leaned forward and poured the last of the wine into my glass. I thought the davenport was going to collapse under the weight of my questions: "Was it important? Is anything important? What does it all mean? What does anything mean? Does anything mean anything? Was it a *piccola avventura* that turned out to be a *grande passion* or a *grande passion* that turned out to be a *piccola avventura*? A story like mine should end with a comes-to-realize moment. But I haven't realized anything."

"Or a fails-to-realize moment," she said.

"But if it's fails-to-realize, that means there must have been something to realize, something I missed. Doesn't it?"

"Stay calm and carry on," she said.

"Sorry," I said. "I'll be all right."

"How about this, little brother: Maybe it's like money in the bank, a savings account, or an IRA or a money-market fund at a brokerage house. When you need some emotional capital, you'll be able to draw on it." She stood up. "But I'm going to bed."

"Sleep tight," I said. "Don't let the bedbugs bite."

That night, lying in the bottom bunk of the old cedar bed that matched my old cedar desk, I read for a while—Thucydides' *History*. In Rex Warner's translation. A book I'd read in my first year at Michigan. But I didn't get very far. I turned out the light. The silence was unnerving— an occasional car on Kruger road, the lights swishing across the room, the usual creaks of an old house, my sister closing and opening the bathroom door. I listened harder, kept listening harder and harder till I could hear Rosella's voice in my ear: "*Whun ye feel it coomin, luv, tock it oot,*" till I could hear my mother playing *The Harmonious Blacksmith* on the piano downstairs, till I could hear Gracie sobbing at the kitchen table after Pete left her and moved up to Battle Creek, and someone who was not Bob Dylan singing "Corrina, Corrina" on an Italian website, and the sharp whistle of the coal mine at the Museum of Science and Industry, and Elena grunting with pleasure as she chomps down the apples that I hand-feed her, and even the *clack clack clack* of my father's typewriter in his little office off the front hall, and I knew that I had nothing to lose, that nothing is ever lost.

JAMES KIMBRELL
Free Checking!

Desire for the good deal, the hot need
to look slick, wordless advertisement
for the invisible product, I release you
like the dumpster behind the cafeteria

releases these long, festering rivers of milk.
Fear of death, fear of narrow spaces, love
of the wine-red mole that punctuates
the transaction-inspiring cleavage of Jill,

my credit union teller, I release you like
the scared-shitless man releases the tiny
parachute. The name "James Kimbrell"
which I share (says Jill) with thirty-eight people

in Florida alone, the subsequent deflation
of our hero groomed by the goddess,
sped by the wind, loved by his mutt, envy
of his entire dreamed-up Mediterranean—

I release you like the crank-addled truck driver
releases his cargo at the midnight dock
until the warehouse is one in a trail
of crumbs, little light left on behind him.

JAMES KIMBRELL
Chicken Brick'n

Because there's no end to cruelty,
      Lyle ties half a brick
            to a hen's foot, climbs

the ladder up the water tower
      where waits Tony—together,
            they toss their weighted hens

into space: the flung chicken
      that charts its course
            across clear air, fans its wings

and flaps a few feet
      with all the glory of a crippled
            helicopter, thereby traversing

the greater distance before
      its feathers flip skyward
            and the dud parachute

of its body descends to the weeds
      with a certain thump,
            that chicken will be crowned

—posthumously, of course—
      Chicken Brick'n Champ.
            In some cases, boredom

might be life at its best,
      all the suffering fixed
            in the doomed body of one noble,

if small-brained, bird.
       I see the three of us walking
              in high grass. Lyle calls

Tony a loser. Tony predicts victory.
       We run toward feathers,
              ready for the measure, T-shirts

pulled over our heads
       in the hooded manner
              of the great Pharaohs.

Gods of wingéd dignity,
       have mercy. We take our
              positions. We count our steps.

JAMES KIMBRELL
Smote

When Shirley Weems submarines her Barbie
in the shallows, spooking the catfish
while her brother and me sit on upturned buckets
with cane poles on our side of the pond
not bothering anybody, I note
how the light around Shirley seems so rosy,
all a-twinkle with its own
self-contained Shirley music. I pick a dirt clod
I don't think contains a rock, but it hangs
long above the pond before completing
its arc, smacking Shirley
upside the head, which sets her off screaming
for the house where her grandfather—big
Truman Weems—barrels out
in these overalls it looks like he's stuffed full
of inflated inner tubes, what you might call
stacked fat, like raw biscuits
pushing against the cardboard tube
after you whack the can against
the counter edge—so puffed out
and defined is Mr. Truman's fat that each roll
trundles separately when he charges
after me, slapping the air, hollering
that I'd better get back across the street,
and where is my mother, I am nothing
but trouble—Little lousy
peckerhead son of a bitch!
                Thank you, Mr. Truman,
for your patience and understanding.
In my defense, I threw the dirt clod
because I never thought it would reach her.
Because she was scaring off all the fish
no one would ever catch anyway.

I threw it because she was so pretty,
or lonely, or I was.
I tried to lob it more or less around her,
and yet with that one mistake
I joined the ranks of the rock throwers,
and it shook me so biblically
I thought I'd dreamed it.
                          Even the Guernsey cows
grazing in the pecan orchard between
my house and the cemetery
seemed suspicious,
disappointed. Those sweet drowsy cows,
weed munchers, cows never milked,
old absent-landlord cows, they stare
at me now with no more comprehension
or pardon than on that day
when I found
the very reach of the earth vaster, more
unforgiving than I ever
imagined in the tall grass littered with rotten pecans
where I lay at the feet
of the animals.

KENT LEATHAM
Sappho 16

Some say the Army

                    and some the Marines

and some say the Air Force is the greatest sight
sweeping over this crippled earth

but I say love

            for example

                      a wedding

the bride's face hidden
as though no longer
hers to share

             and the sound of wailing

        oh, Anaktoria

                  what have they done

the soldiers

            on your wedding day

ELIZABETH McCRACKEN
Hungry

The grandmother was a bright, cellophane-wrapped hard candy of a person: sweet, but not necessarily what a child wanted. She knew it too. That sad bicentennial summer, her son in the hospital recovering from surgery, she and her granddaughter looked for comfort all over Des Moines: at the country club, the dinner club, the miniature-golf course snack bar, the popcorn stand at the shopping mall, the tearoom at Younkers, every buffet, every branch of Bishop's Cafeteria. What the girl liked best: to choose your own food, not just chocolate cream pie but a particular, considered wedge. To stand before the tall, toqued brunch chef, who minted Belgian waffle after Belgian waffle and rendered them unto you. The world of heat-lamped fried chicken and tall glasses of cubed Jell-O and dinner rolls with pats of butter so refrigerated you had to warm them in the palm of your hand before they'd spread. The girl had already split one pair of pants. It didn't seem to bother her. "Oh, well," she'd said, reaching around to verify the rent. "Never mind."

Now here was Lisa, aged ten, the morning of the Fourth of July, 1976, zaftig, darling, oblivious, dressed for the occasion as some founding father: navy polyester pants knickerbockerishly tucked into tube socks, a pair of red-and-white espadrilles that had run in the rain, a thin ruffled lavender shirt borrowed from Sylvia herself. The outfit showed every ounce the girl had put on in the past month. She'd come from Boston to be taken care of while her father was in the hospital. Instead, the two of them had eaten all the things Aaron—sweet Aaron, the grandmother's oldest—could not eat.

"Who are you, sweetheart?" Sylvia asked. "George Washington?"

"Patrick Henry!" said Lisa. "I'm going to perform his Glorious Speech at the block party."

"You're going to what?"

The girl began to hunt through the fruit bowl in the middle of the dining room table. "I have it memorized. I did it for the fourth grade talent show."

"Did you win?"

"Did I *win?*" Lisa thumbed a grape loose from its fellows and chewed it. "It wasn't a contest," she said at last. "People clapped."

"I don't understand," said Sylvia. "You want to say the speech at the party? You can't just start shouting."

"I won't shout."

"You can't just make everything stop so people will look at you," said Sylvia.

"Oh," said Lisa, "you'd be surprised." She pinched off another grape and ate it.

The fruit bowl was an attempt to offset the buffets. Aaron wouldn't mind, probably, nor his wife, Marjorie, who was herself plump, but if Aaron's sister found out that their mother had overseen a notice-able weight gain—well, Rena had already suggested that Sylvia was responsible for Aaron's bad heart, even though their father, Sylvia's husband, had his first heart attack even earlier, at forty-two, and died of his third twenty years later. According to Rena, their childhood was one long period of Sylvia like a mad bomber installing explosives in the bodies and souls of her children, set to go off when they became adults. Sylvia wondered how long it might take to return Lisa to her original condition.

Sylvia still filled the candy dish in Lisa's room, but with dietetic caramels and sugar-free fake M&M's. She bought a brand of soda pop called Kalorie Kounter, in cans festooned with tape measures that floated like banners in an old oil painting. For the block party this afternoon, she and Lisa together had made a lo-cal noodle kugel: low-fat cottage cheese, fat-free sour cream, margarine, a cornflake topping.

Terrible, unutterable words: *fattening, lo-cal, dietetic.* And anyhow, every day, Mrs. Tillman across the hall called Lisa over and fed her orange marshmallows shaped like enormous peanuts, and Pixy Stix. Lisa's first day in Des Moines, Mrs. Tillman had knocked on the apart-ment door. "I have suckers," she'd said. "You have what?" asked Sylvia. "Suckers, suckers," said Mrs. Tillman, digging in the pockets of her housecoat. When she pulled out her hand, she'd caught a number of lollipops between her knuckles by the sticks. All yellow. Either they were cheaper to buy that way or she'd already eaten the good colors herself.

Thereafter, Lisa went to visit Mrs. Tillman every morning. "She loves it here," Mrs. Tillman always said, a note of competition in her voice. Mrs. Tillman's late husband had owned an appliance store, and she had retained an appliancelike air, functional, awkward, a woman to be moved around on a dolly. *I am the grandmother,* Sylvia thought but didn't say. *That is the winning hand. That beats all other old ladies, no matter what.* Then she and Lisa would go out and flag the ice-cream truck. Fudgsicle for Lisa, Dreamsicle for her.

"Why don't you do the speech for me?" Sylvia asked Lisa now. She sat down on the sofa, her hands clasped. "Then you can just enjoy the party."

"No, thanks. Daddy says I should save it for the performance."

"What performance?"

The girl shrugged. "He taught me Hamlet's speech to his players too. 'Speak the speech, I pray you.'" Another grape. This one she tossed in the air: it bounced off her chin. "Oops. Anyhow, it was his idea, when I told him about the party. So I better."

"He doesn't understand—"

"Grandma," the girl said seriously. "You have to do what sick people ask."

In earlier years, Sylvia had been a one-foot-in-front-of-the-other person. When disasters happened (her mother had taught her), you strode firmly in the opposite direction, because calamity followed catastrophe followed disaster. People who believed things couldn't get worse were the ones who were killed, by man or nature. You had to get away.

But this Bicentennial summer, all she could think was *my fault.* She could hardly move for culpability. That's what happened when you were the oldest surviving member of your family. You could not cast blame any further back: it was yours, like your spinster aunt's diploma. Everyone else refused it, and the only way to hand it down was to die.

She'd fed that boy, her son, too well. That's what Rena said: she'd starved the girl and stuffed the boy. Last Thanksgiving, Rena had come with her steno notebook full of all the ways that Sylvia had damaged her, as though at the end she might present her mother with a bill. *Distrust of men:* $9000. *Fear of living alone:* $15,000. "I need to do this," said Rena, and she flipped page after page and listed wounds: how Sylvia and Ben had always taken Aaron more seriously; how in the family, you had to be careful about hurting men's feelings but women didn't matter; how they hadn't bought her a piano when that was all she really wanted. Aaron wanted a dog, he got a dog. Aaron wanted a car, he got a car.

"I don't remember you ever asking!" Sylvia had said.

"You knew," said Rena darkly. Then she added, "You never loved me unconditionally. There were always strings."

"What are you talking about? Darling, I absolutely loved you. *Love* you."

"You didn't love me the way you loved Aaron."

What could Sylvia say? That was true. Not more nor less but differently. If one could measure love—but even then love was too various, one love would have to be measured by degrees Fahrenheit and one by atomic weight. First born, second, boy, girl: of course different loves. To compare was nonsense. What Rena wanted: scales with packages of maternal love, finally squared—but then she'd complain about something else. *You just gave me the same love you'd already given Aaron! You didn't treat me like an individual!*

A different love for grandchildren too: Unreserved. Gleeful. Greedy. Sylvia was allowed to rub Noxzema into Lisa's sunburnt back after a day at the swimming pool. She let Lisa pick out expensive shampoo at the grocery store, something called Milk Plus that smelled like the 1930s baby soap she'd washed her children with. So what if Lisa'd fallen asleep with the bubble gum they'd got from the candy store, and it ended up in her hair and had to be cut out? They walked down to Sal's salon, and now Lisa had her first real haircut from a professional. They cuddled on the orange guest bed and watched television and ate popcorn. Oh, if Rena ever found out how Sylvia loved the childish flub of her granddaughter, the dense bakery heat of her limbs, her neck like a loaf of bread—a voracious love, a near starvation, though here the girl was in front of her. That was what the love of children was like, in Sylvia's experience, and she supposed it made sense that Rena was sad, such mother love had to end, to mellow. You couldn't bite a grown-up. You couldn't sniff at an adult woman's neck. If she went to Rena's therapist—that was who had insisted on the steno pad, the formal accusation—she surely would have hated to hear what it meant, her longing to bite children. To devour them. She nibbled, she tickled, she nuzzled, she inhaled. That was the real end of childhood, wasn't it, when you looked at a stringy kid and loved her but didn't want to bite.

But it pained her too, the pudge of her granddaughter's thighs. The straps of her bathing suit cut into her shoulders, and her face had changed. She'd been so casual about the split pants, as though it happened all the time. At ten weight didn't matter so much, and of course, a smart girl like that was more than her body. Rena had said, *You made it seem as though your love for me was dependent on my weight!* No, of course not. A mother loves her children no matter what. *But* other *people, darling Rena,* she wanted to say, *other people* did *care, other people might well love you less.* Her job as a mother—she believed this then, believed it now—was to make sure that her children would be loved by the maximum number of other people. This was the source of all of her anxiety.

They would get the weight off before it was time for Lisa to go home, she'd decided. Surely that was possible.

They were getting ready to leave for the block party when the phone rang.

"Hold on!" Sylvia called. The nearest phone was in the kitchen.

"I'm going to see Mrs. Tillman," Lisa said, and Sylvia tried to give her a wave that said both *all right* and *don't ruin your lunch.*

"Mama," said Rena on the phone. "I need you to be calm. All right?" But Rena's own voice was not calm. Sylvia took off her sunglasses and replaced them with her indoor ones. She sat at the kitchen table. The phone cord just reached.

"Mama," said Rena. "It's Aaron. Mama, things do not look good."

The clock on the kitchen wall was shaped like a frying pan. Why on earth, Sylvia wondered, what could it mean, a clock like a skillet?

"He's on a ventilator," said Rena. "But—they'll take him off it. This afternoon, probably."

A heart attack, a little heart attack, like his father's first one. A good heart attack, the kind that could scare you into behaving. Sylvia cleared her throat. "And then what happens?" she asked.

Rena let out a long rattling noise, halfway between a sigh and a moan, which Sylvia understood as another accusation of maternal crime.

"Mama—"

"What do the *doctors* say?"

"Well, he'll stop breathing," said Rena. "So."

"I'll call the airline," said Sylvia. "I'll hurry. Lisa's—no, we'll drive to the airport right now—"

"We need you to stay there," said Rena.

"We? Who?"

"I've talked to Marjorie. That's what she wants."

"Where are you?"

"I'm here at the hospital. I drove up last night, when things started to look bad."

"Rena!" said Sylvia, and now she was standing up, the phone cord wrapped around her hand (that twisted, loved, comforting phone cord, like a length of worry beads). "Rena, of course I have to be with him, I *have* to—"

"Mom," said Rena. "No."

"I can help! If she'll let me! *Aaron,*" said Sylvia, as though that was the problem, a mother needed to say her dying child's name aloud, to call him back to life.

"This isn't about you," said Rena, in her kindest voice.

Well, who was it about, then? That was the thing: Rena always remembered that Sylvia was their mother but somehow forgot that this meant they were Sylvia's children.

"And you *can* help," said Rena. "Keep Lisa with you, and happy. Tomorrow—when it's over, it would be wonderful if you could bring her home. All right?"

"What do I tell her?" said Sylvia.

"Nothing. That's very important, Mom. All right? Marjorie needs to figure out what to say. *She's* the mother."

"All right," said Sylvia. "OK. You'll call me?"

And then Rena's voice fully broke, and she said, "Of course. You'll be the first one. I'll see you soon."

There were only eight units in the building, all with the same floor plan, identical or mirrored, depending. To see what other people did with their apartments was disconcerting, a separated-at-birth moment. Your life would look like this if you weren't you. She could hear dim mechanical sounds inside Mrs. Tillman's apartment after she rang the bell. What was her first name anyhow? Sylvia imagined a tag on her that said (like her husband's goods) TILLMAN. That's what brand of woman she was. Sylvia was doing her best not to cry. She had a few seconds more of doing her best on her own.

The door opened to reveal Mrs. Tillman, behind her a wall of hung decorative plates, each with a scene of Hummels through the seasons. China plates with china figurines. Sylvia was panting, she realized.

Then she reminded herself that she had a job: to keep Lisa happy.

"Ah!" said Tillman. Her hair was coral-colored. She leaned on a walker that seemed too short for a tall woman. It gave her a restrained look, as a lunatic is restrained in a sanitarium. "Hello, Syl. We had a little problem."

Sylvia wondered, for a moment, whether Mrs. Tillman had had a stroke; then she saw that she'd merely applied her lipstick off-center.

"We had a little problem," Mrs. Tillman repeated. "We used something without permission. Talcum powder." She gestured at a dusty-headed, teary-eyed Lisa, who stood by a garish bird-patterned sofa. *Lisa knows,* thought Sylvia. *How does she know?*

"I wanted to look like I had a powdered wig," said Lisa.

"Ah!" said Sylvia. "Did you say you were sorry, darling?"

Lisa nodded.

"So we had a little spank," said Tillman in a bright voice, "and now we are friends again."

A little…spank? Sylvia tried to make sense of this. Tillman nodded encouragingly, and then mock-spanked the back of her own wrist, to illustrate.

"You *spanked* her?" Sylvia looked at the plates again, and saw them for what they were: portraits of children who in five years would join the Hitler Youth, little lederhosened, dirndled monsters. She wanted to pluck them one by one from the wall and smash them, and then she realized the strange feeling in her arms was her hands, which were heavy as sandbags and had been since she'd hung up the phone. Grief had made them huge. They felt ready to drop off her wrists. Lisa couldn't get out, not past the walker, which seemed not the support of an elderly woman but a torture device to be used on small children. Sylvia reached over and picked the walker up and moved it closer to Tillman's body.

"Syl!" said Tillman, stumbling back, and so Sylvia grabbed her by the wrist. The other hand she held out for Lisa, who took it and was out of the apartment and under her grandmother's wing, smelling of ticklish, tickling babyhood.

"Are you crazy?" Tillman said. "Let go!"

Sylvia was still holding Tillman's wrist. She felt she could snap it. The ulna of a Hummel: of course china people had china bones.

"I'll call the police!" said Tillman.

"*You?*" said Sylvia. "Call them! I'll have you arrested!"

"You're hurting me! Let go!"

"Call the police!" Sylvia said. "You don't *spank* someone else's child! Nobody's! It's barbaric!"

"Grandma," said Lisa. "It didn't even hurt! Please!"

Sylvia flung Tillman's wrist back at her, and the door closed. From the other side they heard Tillman say, "The police? You call the police on me, I'll call them on you!" A thud: she must have struck the inside of her door; then they heard the chain lock slide closed.

They stood in the hallway together, Sylvia and Lisa, not yet bereaved.

"Let's just get out of here," said Lisa. "Let's go to the party. Let's go the back way."

Poor girl, thought Sylvia, but she meant herself.

She was returning to her body. Her hands still felt oversized, but filled with helium. All she really wanted was to go to her apartment, to her bedroom, to the back of her walk-in closet, to sit among the shoes. She thought she might feel better if she gnawed on one.

No. They had to keep busy. That was the only way they might manage. She didn't know what a ventilator was, exactly. Did it go over your face? Down your throat? Whenever she heard the words *life support*, she pictured a series of cords attached all over a sick person's body, all leading to one enormous plug in the wall: that was the plug that was pulled, when you pulled the plug. Suddenly she understood life support as something that involved a certain amount of brute force. A shim, a brace. The phone might be ringing in her apartment even now. They walked away, down the back steps. When her children were little and first came home from school to tell her things they'd learned—for instance, that Ponce de Leon had come to the United States on Columbus' second voyage—she'd always felt unnerved: they knew things she didn't. Now they still did. Aaron would die. He would die. (She repeated this in her head a few more times.) And apparently, this death was not about her and not about Lisa.

They were outside now, in the sun. The street smelled of gunpowder and lemonade. Little kids held their hands in the bright showers off sparklers. Everyone else was in shorts and sleeveless shirts, Sylvia saw. Nobody else was in costume.

"Don't eat anything with mayonnaise," she told Lisa.

"Because it's fattening?"

"It goes bad in the heat. You could die from hot mayonnaise. No potato salad. Listen, darling. It isn't right that Mrs. Tillman spanked you. No one has the right to spank you, all right?"

Lisa nodded seriously. Then she said, "Can you fix my queue?"

"Your what, darling?"

"My pigtail." The girl turned and presented her back. Sylvia tightened the sad braid, the brown hair slippery under the talc, faded, like a sun-damaged photo. The bow was blue. Her shoulders were broad. Sylvia stroked them. Without turning around, Lisa said, "My dad spanks me sometimes."

"Well," said Sylvia, shocked, "did you deserve it?"

But Lisa was already hopping away on her smudged espadrilles toward the dessert table.

She came back with a cream puff—cream puffs! worse than tuna salad!—and with Bill Antoni, the superintendent of the building, a retired custodian. He and his wife lived in the basement, next to the all-purpose room and the storage lockers. He was wearing a tank top that said FORD across the chest, the word buckled by the curve of his belly. Even from this distance, the mustache that hid his upper lip looked dirty.

"George Washington here has a question for you!" he said to Sylvia.

"Patrick Henry," said Lisa.

Sylvia looked at Lisa, as seriously as she could: as much seriousness as Lisa could hope for herself, or for Patrick Henry. "What is it, sweetheart?"

"Can I have a sparkler?"

"Of course."

"Told ya," said Bill Antoni. He smiled at Sylvia, with a little wink like an afterthought.

Should she tell him? A mad spanker in the building. Surely he should know so he could attend to it, the way he attended to the furnace and the landscaping. But she felt the moment she opened her mouth she would unravel, tell him everything, fall into his arms. Bill Antoni's mustache was nostril-damp in two channels. He was fat, healthy, alive. The sound of a police siren came winding from the distance, and Sylvia wondered whether it had been hailed by Tillman, coming for her.

Bill Antoni handed Lisa the thin wire of the unlit sparkler. "Hold steady. That's it. Hey, there's going to be dancing later."

Lisa stared at the spot where the stick met Bill Antoni's lighter, and said, "I don't dance," and Sylvia thought that was the saddest thing she'd ever heard, and besides, *Don't stare at fire.*

The sparkler caught. Lisa held on to it with both hands, as though it were a responsibility, not a pleasure. *Yes,* thought Sylvia: *my fault, my fault.* She had made Aaron, and Aaron had made Lisa (though Sylvia herself had no sense of being made by her parents, only loved). If Rena had been there with the steno pad, Sylvia would have signed it, like a confession, and demanded, at last, her punishment. Surely her crimes were capital. She wished to burn like the sparkler, beautifully, fatally. They all watched.

When it sputtered out, Bill Antoni said to Lisa, "What do you mean, you don't dance?"

"I'm more into forensics," she said.

He scratched his head with the hand that held the lighter. "Like dead people?"

"Speeches. I give speeches. I'm going to give one today. I have it memorized."

Sylvia thought this would put an end to it. Bill Antoni would make it clear: this is a block party, not a debate meet, you strange, strange child.

"Well, why not?" he said. "Come this way. That all right with you, Grandma?"

I am not your grandma, thought Sylvia, but she nodded. A moment to breathe. A moment to herself. "Right, then," said Bill Antoni, and he led Lisa away, and Sylvia knew she'd made a mistake. She never wanted a moment alone for the rest of her life.

The last time she'd seen Aaron in person had been at Thanksgiving, in Boston, ice on the ground; on this day, he was dying, it was hot; which would she remember?

They should be inside, to answer the phone. They should be out here, in order not to. She pictured the phone ringing and ringing, Rena forced to stand by one of the hospital pay phones, thinking of her mother, cursing her, "Mom, come on, answer," and Sylvia wanted to fold that girl in her arms too, the one about to lose her brother, my God, there was no loss like that, was there. Sylvia had gone through it herself with her sisters. Aaron's eyes were violet and his hair was black. Had been black before it turned silver. That was why she should be with him now, to see the actual person she was losing, though of course she was losing every version of him: the daredevil baby, the thoughtful ten-year-old, the know-it-all teenager.

There was nothing she could do. She was not in Boston. She could only take care of the girl in Des Moines. As long as they were out here, among the slaws and the Jell-O and the burnt hot dogs, the beguiling array of potato chips, the flags attached to tricycles, made into bunting. Out here Lisa was not fatherless and Sylvia was not sonless. Aaron-less. They hadn't yet sustained that particular damage. Damage: a Rena word, as though any of us made it through life in mint condition. But surely some things were worse than others. As long as Lisa didn't know, she was still perfect. Flawless.

Where was she?

There. In fact, someone *had* put up a little stage, and Lisa was on it. That haircut Sal had given her was terrible, long in back, layers in the front where the gum had been. The talc at her temples was runneled with sweat. She seemed to have dropped a pickled beet down the ruffles of her patriot's shirt. Her eyes were closed.

She was delivering the speech.

A small crowd was listening. A few grandmothers, some of the littler kids. Bill Antoni. An approving man in his thirties who looked like a teacher. It was so hot you could hear the mayonnaise go bad, but there was Lisa, gesturing, serious, saying, "They tell us, sir, that we are weak." July 4, 1976, 43rd Street, Des Moines, Iowa: this girl could start a revolution. Not with her good looks—though, look at her, the beauty!—nor with her smarts, but because she is loved, she is loved, she is—Sylvia looked at Lisa's audience and tried to put this thought in their heads.

Because wasn't that easier? To change a dozen strangers than a single beloved? Look at this wonderful girl. Yes, thought Sylvia, she'd take the blame but she also demanded some credit.

A teenage boy glanced up, saw Lisa, and snorted.

"But as for me," she said, she was pounding her fist in her hand, she believed every word, "give me liberty, or give me death!"

—it was never that easy though, was it, to demand a choice. Ask and ask. You might want both. You might get neither.

At Kohl's Department Store

a father has lost his son. He circles
shoe racks, lingerie, dressing rooms,
calling out "Marco!...Marco!..."
We all want to help, but it's just
too much: Oh, the tragedy of naming
then losing a son named Marco—
born to love and to wander, whole
head submerged in the starched cup
of an outsized Playtex bra, diving
back between a mannequin's legs,
looking *up up* into the filmy constellation
of a polka-dot skirt, deep in the eddy
of perfumes and dyes, and his poor
dumb father who can't be helped,
loping in logical circles, unsuitably tall.

CAMPBELL McGRATH
Aurora Perpetua

O tulip, tulip, you bloom all day and later sway
a deep-waisted limbo above the dinner table,
waiting for a coin to drop into your well,
for the stars to pin your stem to their lapel.

Soon, on ocean winds, dawn cries its devotion,
our world entranced once more into being.
Let go your sumptuous rage, darling.
All this awed awakening is a form of adoration.

What's born in that fountain of salt and spume,
of spackled sea monsters and gardenia perfume,
is everything blossoming ever amounts to:
an hour of earthly nectar, a single drop of dew.

SARAH ROSE NORDGREN
Ghost Lessons

All winter the ghosts were waiting
for a new high-school teacher who

refused to appear, and so you
were roped in. February

had the year on pause, the days
like holes that tripped you over

and over in the frozen yard. You had
no knowledge of history or chemistry

yet were expected to teach
the dead from a colorful textbook,

diagrams resembling medieval castles
or cells. This chapter showed

how every nucleus requires
fortification, the tender ward

and inner structures bordered
by a bright blue membrane.

But no amount of learning, the students
told you, had brought them closer

to the one they all loved—the invisible one
who had no use for books

or the offerings of bread his many
admirers left for him

at the door of the school.
They all watched his empty chair

with awe; his absence took up half
the room. The only proof

they had to show you was
a tidy pile of clothes and hair

like the fur and bone a feeding
owl coughs up. Such a dire love!

But, they said, don't dare pity us. Everyone
must spend their lives devoted

to a magnificent person
who can feel nothing for them.

SARAH ROSE NORDGREN
The Monastery

My hair was not on fire
and the fabric of my shirt
didn't rub me the wrong way.
It was the best day of my life

when I entered the monastery.
My heart was not on fire
but enclosed by a high wall
and covered with new grasses

for the white cow who had
taken up residence there.
Each one of my fingers wished
for exactly the same thing—

to curl around the cold
edges of a dish, spend their long
lives washing bowl after bowl.
I fulfilled their desire

by kneeling in the grass
and taking one bowl down from
the tower at a time. I placed
the clean ones in a row

in the sun. The sun was
on fire and it seemed someone
had taken care to arrange
an exact diorama: My feet

fragile beneath their leather, legs
heavy as pillars, and in my head

the hen whose beak can hold
just one pearl at a time.

TATIANA OROÑO
Aporia

Translated from the Spanish by Jesse Lee Kercheval

Ocean, there is none
without shipwrecks, without the drowned
without victims
there is no

   ocean
that does not lick the shore

   like a sore
or a wound.

TATIANA OROÑO
Elegy for the Road

Translated from the Spanish by Jesse Lee Kercheval

I ask where the things go that did not arrive at their destination. The majority of things. The largest inventory in the world. Where are they going to end up, the things that do not end up anywhere. Those that fail, those that have no remedy. I ask where do they go.

Poetry is the place where the things go that have no solution. To look for it.

TATIANA OROÑO
Without Title

Translated from the Spanish by Jesse Lee Kercheval

The blue sky remained
Everything else

No

BEN PURKERT
Blame Game

Pin the ozone layer on me:
I drove my Hummer into the sky
when I gunned through a red light.
I hit outer space; I clearly went too far.

It's hard to tweeze apart a hole
from the everyday emptiness of air.
Hard to touch upon a hole & not sail
right through. One day or another

every iceberg caves. All that's left
is punching your own face squarely in
the gap between your teeth. Nothing
hurts like a gap, nothing at all.

PETER ROCK
Go-Between

The dogs were all shapes and sizes, all colors. Black and white, brown and gray, they sniffed each other, growled, ran here and there, their paths crisscrossing. Alex and Naomi sat on a bench, their backs against the picnic table; she kept turning away from the river, away from the bridge and the cars sliding overhead, to watch the dogs in the park.

"Look at them," she said. "They're such strange creatures, the way their legs work, how their bodies are fit together. Look."

"Dogs?" he said.

"Sorry," she said, turning toward him. "What did you want to talk about?"

"What?"

"You said you wanted to talk."

That was true. He had called her, asked what she was doing this afternoon.

"How's your grandma's house?" he said. "Is it creepy, at all, living there?"

"I don't know. It's nice having all her old things, I guess, but I keep expecting her to be in the kitchen or come down the hallway. I never had to feed myself, there."

Two long yellow kayaks slipped past. A lady in a bright red hat, a man with a gray beard. Naomi waved, and the man lifted his oar.

"Have you seen Sonja lately?" Alex said.

"We had breakfast this morning. Is that what you wanted to talk about?"

Off to the right was a tangle of bushes and trees, some of them tipping over into the water. Hidden on the other side of those trees, down the river, was an amusement park. Screams rose up every minute or so, every time the people on the rollercoaster made the big drop, headed into the loop.

"I like you," Naomi said to Alex, reaching out to touch his shoulder. "At first, I wasn't so sure, but now I'm really glad we're friends."

"I've known Sonja since second grade," he said, "like almost fifteen years, so I can't tell how things would change between us, start being a different way. It's just weird."

"But you want them to be a different way."

"Obviously."

"What does she think?"

Behind them, people were shouting their dogs' names.

"Did she say anything to you?" he said.

"So you don't know."

"It's just," he said, "we hang out together all the time, and we do that skinny-dipping thing at night—"

"That's like a tradition now—"

"Yeah," he said, "but is it normal for two people our age to take off their clothes and just swim and put the clothes back on, and pretend they weren't naked together at all?"

"For nothing to happen, you mean?"

"I guess so."

"I don't know what normal is," Naomi said, after a while. She laughed. "I guess I don't know what 'nothing' would be, either. I just figured you two knew what you were doing, or you talked about it—"

"That's not the kind of thing she talks about," he said.

Naomi got out her phone, checked it.

"Sonja?" he said.

"No." Naomi smiled. "I have to go pick up my brother from school."

"He's what, seven, now?"

"Nine. Sometimes he acts like he's seven. See you."

Alex watched her walk away, the laces of her Converse trailing behind her. Then he looked up at the cars on the bridge. Red, blue, blue, silver. He gazed down along the bridge's girder to the river, to a sailboat sliding past. And then, off to the right, the bushes began shaking, as if a stray blast of wind had become tangled in them.

A man's pale face stared out from the green leaves, and then his body stepped through. Thirty feet away, he wore a black suit, a white shirt, scuffed black shoes. His tie was loosely knotted, his sparse dark hair slicked back across his balding head. He moved closer to the picnic table, one hand up, then pointing at Alex as he approached. His thick eyeglasses flashed like mirrors, hiding his eyes for a moment, and then there they were, dark, staring through.

"Good afternoon, young fellow," he said.

"Hi." Alex kept facing the river, expecting the man to pass by, but he did not.

"I saw you," the man said. "I watched you, sitting here with your girl, talking."

"Listen—" Alex said.

"I only," the man said. "I only wanted to tell you something."

"I was about to leave."

The man sat down, on the same side of the table, at the end of the bench, where Naomi had been. He took out a folded white handker-chief and wiped perspiration from his high, creased forehead, from the back of his neck.

"Your girl," he said, turning to face Alex. "She's really beautiful, isn't she? I know, I know, you don't like me saying so, that makes you uncomfortable, but I just wanted to say so. You must be very happy. I wanted to talk to someone who was happy."

Alex didn't interrupt the man. To correct him would only encourage him. The man's hand trembled as he gestured, speaking. There was something—a feather, a few feathers—on the shoulder and lapel of his jacket. A plastic bag rested next to him on the bench; transparent, it seemed to be full of breadcrumbs.

"To tell you the truth," the man was saying, "I've been following her all day. I've been thinking of her for a while. I wanted to tell her this, but then I couldn't approach her, couldn't quite do it. I didn't think I'd be able to speak the words."

"You wanted to tell her that she's beautiful?"

"No, no, not that—that's no secret. What I wanted to tell her was that I had a dream about her, weeks ago, before I ever saw her. Will you tell her that, for me?"

Alex kept staring out at the river, uncertain whether or how to reply.

"Of course, that would depend on the dream," the man said quickly. "I understand that. So, in the dream, she was sleeping. That's all, really, only she looked so beautiful, in a white shirt and black tights, curled up on a bed with a red cover beneath her. Her feet were bare, and her arm was bare, her hand folded up so her fingers covered her mouth." He held up his hand, to demonstrate, black hairs along the back of it.

"She was sleeping on her side, facing me, her eyes closed. Behind her on the bed was a camera, and a backpack, and a suitcase. The wall was wooden paneling and I just walked right through that room. I could've touched her, but I didn't, I was so close. I didn't want to wake her."

It was silent for a moment, only the dogs and their owners barking and shouting. The man had finished talking.

"And that's the whole dream?"

"Will you please tell her?" The man smiled now, leaning closer, his large teeth yellow and crooked.

"I have to go," Alex said, standing, beginning to turn away.

"I'd like to tell you a secret," the man said. "If you'd oblige. I didn't know if I would tell you this, but now I think it would be for the best. It won't take long."

Alex thought he'd begun to move away, but his legs had not moved.

"No one else knows this," the man said. "It's something I did, just the other day." Now he held out a metal bottle opener, a folded slip of paper.

Alex unfolded the paper; it was a shopping list: GARLIC, RAISINS, MILK, CEREAL.

"I took those," the man said. "I thought it would make me feel better, having something of hers, but I was wrong. It only made me feel worse. Like some kind of thief."

"Whose are these?"

"Your girl's."

"Naomi's?"

"I've wondered about her name," the man said. "That's a nice thing to have. A nice name too."

"How did you get these things?"

"I've been telling you this. Have you been listening? She came into my dream, and so I started following her because that was what I was supposed to do, that's how it seemed."

Alex folded up the paper and put it in his pocket. He was still standing, and now the man stood and stepped even closer, his voice a whisper.

"I followed her, just the other day, to the house where she lives. She didn't know. She didn't look back. I waited on her front porch, and then I opened the door. Yes, I went inside. Through the living room, past a wheelchair, into the kitchen. I could hear her singing, I could hear the screen door open and then slap shut. I stood there, and then I saw where she was—on the back deck, but I could only see her legs, her

knees bent over the railing, her bare legs and the hem of her shorts. I took the bottle opener from the counter, and the note I gave you.

"There was a glass, and a carton of orange juice on the counter, the print of her lips, a half inch of juice left. I poured myself some, drank it down. I was so much thirstier than I expected, and it was so sweet and cold! She was still singing, you understand; I couldn't tell the words. There was the sound of something dropping, and when I looked up, out the screen door, I saw that her feet were bare, that she'd kicked off her sneakers.

"I stepped closer, so I could look down through the door and see her body, her arms stretched out wide, her beautiful face turned up with its black hair around it, her eyes closed. She was humming, actually, a tune I didn't know. I watched her, and then I turned and walked out through the kitchen, back through the living room, out the front door, back the way I came."

"And that was all?"

"What?"

"That was all you did?"

"No," the man said. "You're quite right. Thank you for reminding me. Because in that moment, standing at the screen door, I wanted to talk to her, I wanted to tell her about the dream that I've now told you about so you can tell her. But I couldn't say the words. I didn't want to startle her, and the words wouldn't come. So I found a picture—

a slide, actually—just a picture I had, and slipped it into the frame of the screen door, where she might find it, so she might know someone had been drawn to her."

Now the man stepped back, picked up his bag of breadcrumbs, and turned away. He looked back only once as he headed toward the bushes.

"Tell her about the dream!" he said.

Alex stood there, watching as the man fought his way back into the green bushes and disappeared. And then the day sped up again, the dogs barking, the sun slipping out from the clouds.

He took out his phone and called Naomi, but she didn't answer. Next, he called Sonja.

"What's up?" she said. "Missing me?"

"Something happened," he said.

"That's pretty vague."

"Something I need to tell Naomi about. Do you know where she is?"

"At the zoo with her brother, I think. I was going to meet her at her house in a little while. Come over and walk with me."

Alex hung up the phone and looked around. It felt as though someone was watching him. A small white dog chased a ball into the bushes where the man had gone; in a moment, it reappeared, tail wagging, with a bigger, black dog at its side.

The skirt of Sonja's yellow sundress kicked out, slapping at Alex's hand as they walked down the narrow sidewalk.

"What happened?" she said.

"Nothing, really," he said. "I told you that. You'll hear the whole thing when I tell Naomi."

Naomi's grandmother had died in the spring, and now it was summer. Naomi was living in the house until her parents figured out whether to sell it. They were afraid squatters would move in if it was unoccupied, since it was so close against the forest. Still, Naomi never locked the doors.

Alex and Sonja went up the steps onto the front porch and in through the door without knocking. Naomi was stretched out, napping on the couch. When they looked down at her, she opened her eyes. She smiled.

"Here," she said, swinging her legs to the side, her feet on the floor, making room as Sonja climbed over the back of the couch.

Alex crossed to sit in the wheelchair, which sat in the corner—the three of them often practiced with it, made up games and timed themselves going room to room. He rolled himself around to face them. On the coffee table between them rested a glass half full of water, a book of dog breeds.

"So," Naomi said. She wore jeans and a white hoodie, her black hair in her face. The couch cushions slumped down so she and Sonja were caught in the middle, pressed against each other; Naomi lifted her right leg and put it over Sonja's left.

"So." Alex kept his hands on the rubber wheels, turning the chair a little from side to side as he spoke. "This afternoon at the dog park, after you left—this man in a suit came out of the bushes and talked to me."

"What kind of suit?" Sonja said.

"With a tie," he said, "only it was all a little ragged. He wasn't an old man, but he wasn't young. He told me he had a dream about you."

"Me?" Naomi said.

"Yes."

"What was I doing?"

"Sleeping," he said. "Sleeping on a red bed, wearing black tights and white shirt, and your hand was twisted up like this, your fingers covering your mouth." He tried to show her. "You were sleeping, and he walked through the room."

"What did I do?"

"Nothing. You didn't wake up; you just slept."

"He saw me, he saw me at the park?" Alex paused, thinking how he wanted to tell it, how much he wanted to say. He glanced toward the kitchen, through the doorway, the counter visible. A crack in the paint crossed the wood frame of the doorway and climbed across the plaster of the ceiling, forked along the stairway, into the shadows of the second floor above.

"I don't even have any black tights," Naomi said. "I haven't for a long time. Not even leggings."

"The thing of it was," Alex said, "he said he dreamed about you, and then later he saw you and recognized you from his dream. That's when he started following you."

"So he was watching you from the bushes?" Sonja said.

"Why didn't he just talk to me?" Naomi said. "He could have just told me. I mean, maybe I had a dream about him too."

"He said he couldn't do it," Alex said, "that he was unable to approach you. That's why he talked to me."

Outside, a dog started barking. It got louder, as if it were close, in the front yard, and was gradually not quite as loud, fading away down the street.

"He knows that you live here," Alex said. "I think he's followed you for a while."

"Creepy," Sonja said. "How excellent."

"What else did he say?" Naomi said.

"He came inside one day, into this house, a day when you weren't here. He drank a glass of orange juice, and he took a shopping list, and a bottle opener." Standing, Alex pulled them from his pocket, held them out to Naomi. "He told me he left a picture behind so you could find it."

"I didn't find anything," Naomi said, reading the list. "Where are you going?"

In the kitchen, Alex opened the wooden door to the back deck. At first he didn't see the slide, and then he did, and he pulled it loose, held it up to the light: a little girl with her shirt off, a necklace around her neck, her long hair pulled back. In a bowl next to her, bulbs were growing, stalks without flowers yet, sticking into the air.

"What are you doing?" Sonja called. "Checking the raisin supply?"

"Come back in here," Naomi said.

When he handed them the slide, Naomi switched on a lamp, swung the shade around. They squinted, their heads pressed close, their darker and lighter hair mixed together. They were quiet for a moment, concentrating.

"Did I give this to you?" Sonja said.

"What?" Naomi said.

"I didn't think so." Sonja looked up at Alex. "Did you just take it from my place?"

"What are you saying?" Naomi said.

"This is me," Sonja said. "From when I was a girl. I remember that time. I do. And that necklace is amber—I still have it."

"You were so cute," Naomi said, her face close to the light.

Alex sat in the wheelchair again, watching them. Sonja reached out, tucked a strand of Naomi's hair behind her ear, left that hand on the back of her neck. The way they were sitting, the way they didn't even seem to know that he was there, watching them, that he was even in the room with them.

"Only I don't remember anyone taking the picture," Sonja said. "I didn't know anyone was there."

"Your eyes are closed," Naomi said, pointing to the slide. "And back then, even, you liked to take your clothes off."

"We should call someone," Alex said. "Do you think we should call someone?"

"Why?" Naomi said. "About what?"

"Just the man, I guess," he said. "I don't know."

"Where'd you get the picture?" Sonja said.

"On the screen door, like the man told me."

"The man," Naomi said.

"Yes," Alex said. "He came right in here and left it."

"You said he was afraid to talk to me," Naomi said.

"That's what he said."

"I've been waiting," Sonja said, leaning back, her hand around Naomi's, "waiting for something like this to happen. I felt like something was happening. It's so exciting, and now we have to figure out what to do, how to find him."

"We do not," Alex said. "That's not what we have to figure out."

"Are you afraid?" Naomi said.

The two of them were all entwined again, almost whispering, deciding what to do or what not to do, what was the difference between dangerous and exciting. Alex stood and stepped to the door. He waited for them to notice, to call out after him, to say he shouldn't leave. He listened hard, but their voices only grew softer as he went out the door, across the porch and down the steps, onto the sidewalk. He turned once—the trees in back grew over the house, branches scratching at the rooftop—and then walked away from Naomi's house, where they were still talking to each other.

TONY SANDERS
Please and Thank You

Say no now and you will get off easy. Maybe.
The firebrand in your heart is only a rental,
Just a spent ember with nothing left to do
Than plead guilty, not no contest. Now go,
Go to your room and gawk, or else text-message
Yourself, write runes, or if the rhinencephalon
In your boiling brain dictates, write filth,
Stinky warm-ups for prurient graffito
That will never see the light of day or night
While you, useless firefang, squat doggy-style
On your own griddle and sizzle like meat,
Cheap street meat, rancid beef bought fast
On the sly, or better still, five-fingered
And smuggled home against your belly,
The underbelly of a pound hound in heat,
Unable to perform but bound to act out,
Beat your chest and howl, then yelp, then
Whimper until the whimper runs dry,
Your whole world wails and grows silent,
No longer hot, but numb. Now, pal, I like you.

JACOB SUNDERLIN
  The Sacred Harp Book

If I get religious for a minute, it will be to keep terms
with the bewildered caul of being

thirteen, surrounded by the dead. What used to
peek through the roof, never so much

stroking string things and eating afterlife
biscuits, as making sound like a wonky piano

dragging its broken leg in an interminable circle
of Sundays. I could be that throat sound a lame dog

makes in a shitty winter, played through
an amplifier hung in the cold needles

of a silver pine tree bought for a realistic Christmas,
the sound of yes-yes bleeps in the tweaking hour,

sounds made as if to say, You got it right—
these cloud bruise songs are difficult,

but you can learn them, you can burn your days off
in these little lung-clutched disasters.

DONNA TRUMP
Seizure

After the winter of the coma when his wife sued for divorce, after the year of weekly grand mal seizures, Isaac had a job. Now he wanted his sons back—Ethan, who just turned five, and Paul, three and a half. The boys observed their father, if somewhat coolly, from photos posted on the wall behind his repair stand. Isaac lifted a bicycle to eye level. Bike spokes whirled to the hushed *tick-tick-tick* of a freewheel ratchet's heart. Ethan's and Paul's faces flickered in clunky zoetropic animation.

Isaac used his good right hand to palpate gear chain wear and lubricate cranky derailleurs. He examined the bike's brakes, replaced a shattered reflector, swabbed the frame and fenders clean. When he was done, he lowered the two-wheeler from its perch and raised the next. His sons watched, and waited.

There was a host of other things Isaac might have wanted back, aside from his boys: his ex-wife Mary Beth, their shared orthopedic surgery practice, full visual fields. The ability to make a confident decision—about anything. Body symmetry. He would have liked to drive again, but since his deployment, even Isaac saw the foolishness in that. Anyhow, all he really wanted back were his kids. Isaac's brother Ben said he'd help.

"What you have to show is that you're reliable," Ben told him on his discharge from the VA Hospital over a year ago. A social worker had set Isaac up in a group home for brain-injured adults in the Northeast neighborhood. A few blocks away, *Minneapolis: Best Biking City in the USA* blinked on and off in the pull-down, glass-paned garage door of Ben's storefront business. In the year of the bad seizures, Ben taught Isaac simple bike repair, but didn't pay him. Not yet.

"Get here when you're supposed to. No chucking wrenches halfway across the repair room when you're angry. When I tell you I want a maintenance check on five bikes, I mean five: not ten, not three. Today, not tomorrow. Do you understand what I'm saying, Isaac?"

Of one thing Isaac was certain. He was getting better every day.

Isaac had spent time with Ethan and Paul periodically since the accident, of course. For the past several months, he had seen them at least once a week. What galled him was that the visits were more like mutual observation through the bars of a cage than actual fathering.

"Boys, give your dad a break," his ex-wife demanded if Isaac's left hand cramped up, or if he tripped. When he and the kids went from playing cards to wrestling to tag and back to card games in a span of fifteen minutes, Mary Beth seemed to consider it a manifesto of Isaac's impaired attention span. But things were different now. Isaac had his own apartment, a paying job as a bike mechanic, a cocktail of drugs to keep the seizures at bay, and a hand from the local disabled veterans advocacy group. He was going after unsupervised visits with his boys.

"What's the point you're trying to make, Isaac?" Mary Beth asked this morning when he called to confirm today's visit. "Your rights as a brain-injured man trump your own kids' safety?"

Whenever he talked to her, he reminded himself she had started divorce proceedings when he was in the coma. It was her lawyer's face he saw when he first came to. Isaac apparently had let loose on the man in an expletive-laced tirade. All Isaac remembered from that first day awake was an insanely loud U2 rendition of "Beautiful Day" followed by a momentous wrenching of body and limbs. A few seconds into the seizure, it all went to black. He didn't wake up again for days, or so he'd been told.

"Isaac, are you even listening? And I'm supposed to trust you, alone, with the boys?"

"I told you, Mary Beth," he said, "I'm not going to drive. The guys at the shop set me up with a Burley for Paul and a Tagalong half-wheeler for Ethan." They'd had to make a special modification of the Burley because Isaac insisted his youngest, Paul, ride in front where he could see him.

"Oh, right," she said, laughing in a way he did not recall from the past. Face it, Isaac, she was known to say: you don't have a clue how I used to laugh. The injury may have short-circuited his power to recall what happened yesterday, but Isaac held on to old memories like deeply buried treasure. Mary Beth didn't used to laugh like that.

"Sure," Mary Beth continued now. "Bike accessories as panacea against a menu of neurobehavioral deficits and the random grand mal seizure with two small children in tow. Perfectly safe."

Maybe it wasn't. But a bike's forward motion, as opposed to a car's, would—most times anyway—halt if the driver went AWOL. Minneapolis offered up a steady stream of Good Samaritan bicycle and pedestrian traffic. That was as safe as he could make it.

"I'm working today," he said. "I'll come by around three. I'd like to take them for a ride. Just the three of us."

"Isaac, why are you doing this? Why now?"

Because he'd practiced all summer so he could ride his own god-damned bike without falling over. Because it was already October, and if he didn't do it today, how would he ever manage to convince anyone of anything in a snowstorm?

Because if the seizures weren't exactly gone, they'd either morphed or were tamed by pharmaceuticals into almost entirely auditory episodes: Bach's first cello suite, "Ave Maria" by the Vienna Boys Choir, the Rolling Stones' "Satisfaction." On infrequent occasion: screams, the screech of grinding metal, nearly insufferable drumming. Even less often: a knock-down, drag-out motor fit. But most of the time—for Christ's sake, at least three quarters of the time—just music, and then it was done.

"I want to be a Dad, Mary Beth. Just give me that, would you please?" And he pressed the key to end the call.

It was minutes before Ben called Isaac to their lunchtime activity that today's seizure began. A march, it was, this time. John Philip Sousa's "Stars and Stripes Forever"—the ending, where the piccolos go wild.

"Isaac, are you all right?"

Isaac steeled his muscles against the transfer of electrical disturbance to the motor area of his brain, but the seizure was over. He heard only his own nervous breaths, and Ben's repeated question.

"Isaac, you OK?" When Isaac turned away, struggling with his ear warmer, helmet, and gloves, Ben put a hand to his brother's shoulder. "Ready to give it a try?"

They snaked the three-car train of Isaac's bicycle—Burley in front, his own two-wheeler in the middle, and the scaled-down, single-wheeled copilot bike in back—through the shop. There were a few hollers of support from the other mechanics.

"Godspeed, Isaac."

"Way to go, man."

"Don't let the lady get you down"—this from a man whose children lived three states away.

Out in the parking lot, Isaac had to get on from the left side, swing his right leg over the crossbar, plant his butt on the narrow saddle and then consciously will the left foot onto the pedal. It's why his balance stunk: kind of useful to have muscle action happen in an instant and not next week. But shortly, he was in gear, one foot up and one foot down, his full weight on the pedals. Isaac circled the parking lot once, twice around before the spasm in his left leg drew his knee into his chest and conducted his center of gravity to the right and into asphalt. The bike train crashed. Grounded, the Burley's left wheel spun like a kid making himself dizzy.

"That wasn't too bad," Ben said.

Isaac cried, but everyone in the shop was used to the volatility of his injured brain. He practiced again and again, foregoing lunch. Finally, Ben told Isaac he thought he was ready, and that he'd say a prayer for him.

"What kind of prayer?" Isaac asked.

"A prayer for deliverance," Ben said.

Isaac saw himself delivering his boys to a picnic at Minnehaha Falls, because Paul used to belly laugh in the baby swing and Ethan loved to stand on the bridge and watch the water drop over the limestone ledge of the falls. To Lake Calhoun for a swim, because at three years old Paul still needed those damn water wings, and what if a big wind came along and blew him out to the middle of the lake? Isaac had to teach him to swim without them. To the new playground near the Plymouth Avenue Bridge, because Ethan would love the water pumps. They'd bring a toy boat, or just use a stick, and the water Ethan pumped would sail the thing half a block through the park's maze of concrete channels. Isaac would wait with Paul downstream, watch his baby's face light up with the delivery of the makeshift vessel. Isaac imagined delivering his boys home to Mary Beth, tired out and happy. Delivering himself back to his apartment, back to work, back to a plan for the next outing.

"Deliverance it is," Isaac said. "Amen."

Isaac got off work at two, only in that instant realizing he'd never make it to Mary Beth's by three. Execute damage control, the voice of his advocate from the VA rang in his head. He called Mary Beth, gave no excuses, just said he'd be there by five. Isaac reviewed the list he'd written and edited over and over in the last few weeks. Everything he needed was now in the Burley, piled up earlier in the day in a corner of the shop: helmets, treats and water bottle, diaper bag with Pull-Ups and diaper wipes, plus the sunglasses he'd bought Ethan and Paul, just in case they needed bribing.

At 2:30 Isaac began the walk to the river, pushing the bicycle train along by his bike's handlebars. On five miles of Mississippi River trails—dedicated, paved, off-road pathways—he kept to the pedestrian lane. It paralleled the bike trail, descending into flats alongside and climbing high bluffs above a silt-brown Mississippi. Once he got into the rhythm of a walk, the limp more or less disappeared and his arms grew used to their posts on the handlebars. He could have ridden, but after weeks of trying to decide which would be, or appear to be, better or safer or smarter, after weeks of waking up in the middle of the night knowing the answer and then forgetting it by morning, Isaac defaulted to walking. He'd always walked in the past. Sure, he was a little slower pushing the bike, but it beat the hell out of all that second-guessing. Isaac took his time, stopping every mile or so for water and the Gummi worms he'd packed for the kids. He crossed back to the east bank of the Mississippi at the Lake Street Bridge, clover-leafed to the right, rolled down and up the final pitch and rise.

Mary Beth sat in a chair on the front lawn with the boys, who played in hats, coats, gloves, and piles of leaves. Isaac waved at them as he crossed the street. His heart lifted two stories when Ethan and Paul called and ran to him.

"Daddy, what did you *build* for us?" yelled Ethan. Paul literally shuddered with apparent anticipation, or maybe he had just peed in his training pants. Isaac understood either. He was tired and couldn't remember if he'd eaten lunch. But he thought it would look natural enough to sit in the grass for a few minutes while the boys checked out the bike.

"You walked that here?" Mary Beth asked, raking her hand through short, thick hair.

"Just up that last hill," he lied.

"That ground's cold, Isaac. You want a chair?" she said.

He couldn't really feel it. "I'm fine."

In minutes the boys found the sunglasses. Why hadn't he carried them in his pocket? Isaac heard the snap of plastic yards away.

"Why'd you have to break them, you big idiot baby!"

The muffled *thump* of a mitten-handed smack. Paul wailed.

Ethan arrived, running. He displayed the shattered pieces of plastic to Isaac. Only steps behind, Paul pulled an arm back in a determined and formidable arc. He landed a punch square on Ethan's rump before he lost his own balance and fell on his face. Isaac thought he might laugh until his pulse ramped up to the high idle of a Harley. Small tornados spun in his head. For a million dollars he couldn't have explained to anyone why all of a sudden he felt so entirely pissed off.

"Now Isaac, don't get angry," Mary Beth pleaded. She knew too much, was the goddamned problem.

Nonetheless, he slowed his breaths, just as he'd been instructed. Panted, even, like Mary Beth when she delivered each of their beautiful boys. It was going to be all right. In through the nose, out through the mouth. All good. Let it go.

The boys waited. Mary Beth watched.

Isaac didn't know what they expected from him. Wipe the dirt off Paul's face? Remind Ethan he's the big brother? Tell them sunglasses cost good money?

"Don't fight," he decided on. Stacked clouds filled graying skies. "And who needs sunglasses anyway?" A gust of cold wind lifted leaves into spirals of color.

"When we goin'?" asked Paul.

"How about NOW?" Isaac shouted, and reached for both of them, but they got away. He stood, with as much fluidity as was left to him. "Sun sets a little after six, Mary Beth," he said. "I'll have them back before then." One hour. He wouldn't have bet a dollar she'd let them go.

"I can see how hard you're trying, Isaac," Mary Beth whispered.

"Fucking A for effort," he said.

"Isaac, please. It's not that I want to keep them from you." She leaned in to him, although they did not touch. "I'm just so afraid these days, and I hate it. It's no way to live, you know?"

He knew. They all needed it: to go, move, forward, anywhere. "See you in an hour," he said. Straightaway Isaac had the boys' helmets on, Ethan perched on tiptoe in back, Paul buckled into the Burley with the diaper bag at his feet. Isaac steadied the bike train, looked both ways and walked it across the street to the trail.

"Who wants to go see the truck on a rock?" Right leg over. Sit. Steady. She was still watching.

"The truck on a rock?" said Ethan. Mary Beth likely drove them past it daily. "That real truck? On that totally huge rock?"

"Yes and yes!" shouted Isaac. Left leg up on the pedal. Count for the boys. Count for their mother. "One, two, three—are we ready?"

His back was to her now. Paul's weight in the Burley helped, but Ethan wasn't exactly stable. "Truck on the rock! Truck on the rock!" he chanted, swaying from side to side with each syllable.

Forward motion. Forward motion.

Isaac's strong right foot pushed down on the pedal. His left foot skidded off the pedal. Jerky stop. Step, drag, step of his left foot along the pavement. Steady. Still watching. Steady. Start again. "Ready, boys? One, two, three—and we're off!" He said the words first this time, as if to make them real. Both feet on the pedals, both feet pedaling. The bike train flew. Paul clapped. Isaac laughed. They tipped only a little when Isaac turned his head to nod good-bye to Mary Beth.

It was two miles down the trail to the Ford plant. Autumn crunched and snapped under five wheels. A few pedestrians offered good-natured smiles. Three separate children pedaled by and yelled some variation of "Cool bike," their heads turned in crash-worthy inattention to the trail. About once every hundred feet, Ethan rang the tinny bell Isaac had installed for him. Paul sat forward, peering out the front screen of the Burley as if willing them on. Isaac pedaled, moving forward. They covered the distance in no time.

Across the road, a bright red Ranger pickup fixed aslant on a granite base advertised the Ford manufacturing plant. Ethan started pointing and leaning a block away. Isaac braked to a smooth stop and got off the bike. He struggled to unbuckle Paul from the Burley.

Brakes screeched. Ethan swerved, then gained the far curb.

"Ethan!"

He'd already begun to climb the base. Isaac snatched Paul in a right-handed choke hold and lurched across the road. His left arm spasmed higher and tighter as Paul's little legs flailed. At the truck, Isaac didn't have a functional hand to pull Ethan down. Noises came out of Isaac that he hoped weren't sobs.

"Need some help, there?" A man wearing a grimy UAW 879 baseball cap rolled down the passenger-side window while his Ranger purred in the long driveway to the factory. "Any of you like to see how that truck was made?"

Isaac met the man's gaze and decided. He opened the truck's front passenger door and plopped Paul onto the gravel-littered floor mat. "Just a minute," Isaac said, and the man nodded.

Mary Beth would have had a fit. *You're not really thinking of leaving the baby, unsecured, in that filthy car with a stranger, are you, Isaac?* Fine. Yes, he was, and it wasn't his fault if she couldn't see what the guy was made of. In two steps Isaac had Ethan off the rock and was back at the open door of the truck. He scooped Paul from the floor and the three of them lined up on the truck's front seat. The boys were all eyes now. Neither had ever been in a car outside the confines of a car seat.

Fifty feet away and across the parkway, the bike remained more or less abandoned on the trail. "Go on, fetch it," said the man to Isaac. "I got the boys. Follow me, and park the bike behind my truck." Isaac came back with the bike to find Paul in the man's arms, playing with his graying beard. Ethan wore his union hat, snug over his own knitted cap. They walked, together, into the plant.

The older man took their jackets, coats, and hats and gave them each a neon red vest and yellow safety goggles. "Don't break them like you did the others," Isaac snapped at the boys. He hadn't meant to speak so curtly, but something was flapping its wings right under his diaphragm. He couldn't breathe; he was suddenly soaked in sweat. Danger sang to Isaac from every corner of the factory floor. Trucks driven by no one, by phantoms, careening around a landscape where everything and nothing was a street. And the noise—good God, the noise: a suffocating, incessant drone, layered with buzzing alarms, the whine and bolt of compressed air wrenches. Garbage cans colliding, metal scraps compacting. Wildly off-key whirring refrains; mechanized sputtered spray in maniacal rhythms. Isaac couldn't recall so much real-world auditory chaos since the night the passing truck blew up his one-tent operating room.

"Ethan!" he yelled, loud even over the din. "Take the man's hand!" He willed his eyes open, his head clear. He clutched Paul with both arms.

"And don't even *think* about letting go," Isaac hissed to his older son. Ethan spun around the older man's index finger. Paul rubbed his eyes underneath the safety goggles and settled in to Isaac's death grip.

The union-hat guy started the tour. Isaac walked along and took in what he could. Most of it he couldn't hear. He concentrated on the smell of Paul's sweaty head, and kept an eye on Ethan from too far away. In increments, station to station to station, the complete vehicle emerged: pieces of the body joined to doors and bumpers, to engines, and finally to wheels. By the end, truck after truck got a quarter tank of gas and a human behind the wheel. Isaac almost relaxed, until he saw the driver's face, no longer attached to his head. The boy's expression, of all things: surprised. Surprised, young, bloodied. Silenced. Everything, suddenly, silent.

And then Isaac saw Ethan, unaccompanied, dancing toward the metal jaws of an assembly-line robot.

Isaac freed up his contrary left hand. He shifted Paul's weight to his right arm. Five long, uneven strides, and Isaac seized Ethan's shoulder. He pulled him away and then close, hard. With one son more or less secured on each flank, Isaac declared the tour over. "What do you say to our guide, Ethan?" Isaac stammered. *Other than 'Get us the hell out of here, please.'*

"I think I'm supposed to…My dad's…" Ethan seemed to struggle for the right answer.

"Good enough," said the stranger. He helped Ethan with his coat, hat, and gloves, and produced a polar fleece blanket sporting a Ford logo for Paul. "Souvenir. Shame he won't remember as much as his big brother."

Isaac and his boys exited the factory into the silence of a snowstorm. A blizzard. 6:10, the sun about to set, lights on everywhere and sparkling like Christmas tree ornaments in falling snow. A foot of it had collected in the hour they were inside. The bike trail was covered, but it looked like a plow had been through on the boulevard. Telltale berms of snow edged the road. Coarse brown sand broadcast for traction was already camouflaged in white.

Ethan ran ahead, packing heavy snow between gloved hands. "Not now," said Isaac. "Your mom's waiting. This might not be easy."

His first-born son turned to him with an expression that was all business. He brushed off the seat of his bike and got on like a little man: no whining; a dawning, likely, of danger. Isaac buckled Paul into the Burley. Wrapped in the blanket, the child only squirmed and sighed. Isaac flipped on the red light attached to the rear of Ethan's seat and, far in front, the white headlight, adjusting them both to strobe mode.

A police car, siren screaming and lights flashing, approached and receded in the southbound lane. Northbound traffic was heavy, and about at a standstill. Isaac walked the bike train from the Ford plant lot out to the street. He caught the eye of a driver in the northbound lane of cars. He tapped on her front passenger window; she crept to a stop and leaned over a cluttered seat toward Isaac. When the window scrolled down, Isaac smelled pumpkins.

"Can I bike in front of you, in your headlights? It's only a mile or two, but the bike path's full of snow."

"Why don't you just ditch the bicycle?" she asked, eyes on the boys. "I'll drive you where you need to go."

"We're all right."

"I'm not so sure this is a good idea," she said.

"I think it'll work." Isaac searched her pretty face. "Best guess, anyway." He smiled his most confident smile.

She made room for him, flipping on her emergency flashers. Isaac hopped on the bike like he used to: left foot already in the pedal as he lifted his right leg over the crossbar in a motion befitting a track star. Pedaling. Moving forward in the snowstorm, into shadows cast by headlights and a color show behind. Quiet but for the spin of tires on ice and snow, for the slow, sonorous hum of people delivering, people delivered on a brilliant night. Exactly when he heard the Hallelujah Chorus, its high notes electrifying half his body and all of his soul, Isaac wasn't sure. Or maybe it was only Ethan behind him, shifting weight from pedal to pedal and singing, straight into the wind.

RONALD WALLACE
Song of Myself

after Issa

I think it's enough just to sit and meditate, heedless
of the needs of others close to us and of
their perpetual demands that seem to sap the
strength from us. My doorway and the morning dew
are all I need to make my day, and that
is where I'll plan to be. And if that marks
me misanthropic, if that threatens to end our
relationship, I say that is not my problem, closing
my door. Thoreau knew how to spend the day
alone with his peas and beans and ledgers, and we
can do the same. So much for the ties that bind.
"We must find our occasions in ourselves,"
said self-reliant Thoreau. And so I'm going to sing to
myself. And the birds. And you. And one or two others.

Note: *The last words of each line, read vertically
top to bottom, form a haiku by Issa.*

JONATHAN WELLS
House of Wigs

The sky was low. His head was a vase of
sorrows he wanted to fill with blossoms.
He stepped into the House of Wigs.
The saleslady said, "Try this one on. It's called
the *Mind of Fire.* It turns ashes into flame.
Prometheus was wearing it, they say, when
he was punished by the Gods for his compassion
and he barely felt the eagle's claws landing
on his stomach."

"This one is known as the *Parable of Spring*
for its rhythm and its pageant. The fresh
grass and forsythia will carry you toward
summer, your body lithe and unencumbered,
your hunger fed by fields of daisies."

"I'm wearing *Love's Crown,*" she said,
"because love shouldn't be a neon idol
shining on a shelf. It must be worn
and worn through and not just the love
you bring but the love you can accept,
especially when the days are short
and brooding. Go ahead," she said.
"Put it on. Stand next to the light."

MIKE WHITE
Reunion

And shall we describe the beautiful bike?
It was a beautiful color the beautiful bike.
What ever happened to the beautiful bike?
The beautiful bike rode off into the beautiful sunset.
Not by itself, surely. Who was pedaling the beautiful bike?
You, you were the one pedaling the beautiful bike
last seen disappearing into the beautiful sunset.

Now I remember the beautiful bike.
Now I can see myself
pedaling like mad the beautiful bike…

Is it OK to cry?
It is always OK to cry.

It is *so* good to see you again.
It is so good to see *you* again.

ABOUT JEAN THOMPSON
A Profile by Ladette Randolph

As a child—"I mean really little," Jean Thompson says, "teething and waking up at night crying"—her sleep-deprived parents put a stack of graham crackers in one corner of her crib and a stack of Little Golden Books in the other. "Whenever I woke up with sore gums, instead of screaming, I'd find my books and my graham crackers and snack and read myself back to sleep." With a typically dry aside, Thompson wonders "what might have been different if they'd put me to bed with, say, a bassoon and a strong cup of coffee."

Given this story, it's not surprising that Thompson's mother taught her how to read before she began school by creating little books with letters and pictures. With such an early start, she was reading the classics before junior high—books that were "way too old for me," she says, "like Chekhov," and books that "seemed about right, like Dickens."

She read anything, including at one point an old Abnormal Psychology textbook on the shelves at home, engrossed by the "painful pictures of morons, imbeciles, idiots, people with hydrocephalus." She couldn't resist reading *Gone With the Wind* when she overheard her mother and her friends talking about it. Eventually, she became so absorbed in books that her concerned parents told her to "quit reading and go outside and play." But, she argues, "Once you are transported by a book, it is a profound and active engagement."

From this early engagement with literature has come a long and distinguished career. Called the "American Alice Munro" by admiring reviewers—a nod toward both her masterful prose and her subject matter, which focuses on the lives of ordinary people, often women, living in the overlooked center of the country—Thompson's stark vision is offset by pitch-perfect dialogue, elegant pacing, and deadpan humor. The setting for most of her stories and novels are places that have been, in some way, left behind, but her honest and generous portrayal of these downtrodden areas and the characters who inhabit them, along with sense of humor, mediates what might otherwise become bleak in her work.

Until she retired in 2006, Thompson taught in the English Department at the University of Illinois. The author of eleven books of fiction, her writing career has built slowly and steadily. She began by publishing in little magazines in her early 20s, eventually catching the attention of *Ploughshares* and *The New Yorker*. From there, she gained the notice of the *Best American* and Pushcart prize anthologies. Despite prize attention, stellar reviews for her books, and the respect of other serious writers, it wasn't until 2001, when her short-story collection *Who Do You Love* was nominated for the National Book Award, that she began to attract wider notice.

In 2003, her novel, *The Wide Blue Yonder,* was recognized by the *New York Times* as a Notable Book and was a Best Fiction selection of the *Chicago Tribune.* Since then, with the publication of two more acclaimed short-story collections and three more novels, her reputation has only grown. Reviewers have praised her as a warm-hearted, "masterful storyteller" capable of "literary heights" with an "ear for the worries of small-town dwellers," whose "comic timing...simultaneously captures the colloquial tone of her character's inner monologues and skewers their limited worldview without ever losing affection for [them]." With an impressive and growing body of work, she seems poised to be among the contemporary writers most likely to be remembered by future generations.

Serious writing first came for Thompson in a fiction workshop in college, which she signed up for only because her roommates were already in it. Later, she applied to graduate schools in writing because a friend of hers had the idea. "I'd like to think I would have figured things out on my own, eventually," she says, "but there's no telling."

Her workshop teachers were all, "almost without exception, tough-minded, generous, encouraging," and she goes on to ask if it would surprise her sister writers that these teachers were all men, that there "were no women teaching poetry or fiction at either school." She adds, "the visiting writers were [also all] men, save one, and that was Joyce Carol Oates." And "no one, including myself, thought this was remarkable at the time."

Thompson is philosophical about a career that has built slowly over time rather than overnight, concluding that she feels fortunate for having "served a pretty long apprenticeship in terms of writing and publications." Ever gracious, she acknowledges in an online interview with Susan Tekulve for *Web del Sol* that she's "been fortunate to have a long career of writing fiction" with "some nice pieces of recognition" along the way. She believes that, if she's had any success, it's "because I never stopped never stopped never stopped writing." If you keep writing, she adds, "you can't help but get better."

Thompson describes herself as a "brick-by-brick writer," by which she means she can't move on until the work she's done previously is sound. She usually begins each day by re-reading a story or a chapter from its beginning, making changes along the way, before moving on to the next thing.

For young writers, Thompson's long career is instructive. Her work, rather than diminishing with time, is instead gathering energy and authority. "I think I've gotten slower but surer as a writer," she says. "I seem to need a steady sense of momentum with my work, and to keep in touch with it on a daily basis. If you make your best conscious effort, as Graham Greene said, then your subconscious does its work and presents you with solutions."

As for her personal writing schedule, she says, "The trick is not to sabotage yourself by engaging in necessary but distracting household chores, or reading newspapers online. I have reasonably good work habits and self-discipline, plus if I slack off or give my work less than my best effort, self-loathing sets in." Her routine is movable: "I don't have a dedicated writing space," she says, in an interview on the blog *Catching Days*. "The computer sits on the dining room table, but the yellow legal pads that I use for first drafts get dragged all over the house, and I perch (or recline) with them in different places."

When asked in an online interview how she finds her material, Thompson says, "Obviously, there's a great distance between the original impulse for a story and the carrying out of it. This is the way of stories. There's a beginning place, and then you build on that. The impulse is what guides you through a story...If you are a writer, you make use of what comes your way. Your job is to process experience, as opposed to the journalist who goes out to research a story...I think a writer's job is to say 'here is the world that I filter through my instrument of writing,' and try to order and make sense of it in an aesthetic way."

In the same interview, she says that she considers writing a form of exploration: "I think my work...is a way of getting inside someone else's experience. It's always wonderful for me to see how people construct the narrative of their lives." Refusing to remain bound to a certain region or mode of fiction, her imagination has continued to expand into new areas. "I've been working on stories that are, perhaps versions, perhaps corruptions, of traditional fairy tales. What if," she asks, "Hansel and Gretel were neglected children who ended up in the foster care system? What if Little Red Riding Hood hung around Internet chat rooms, doing funky things online?" Asked about the dark turns in many of her stories, Thompson replies, "Fiction is a way of working through what is difficult or oppressive, or challenging about life, at least for me."

Thompson often writes about the difficulties and complexities of love. Though there are no uncomplicated happy endings in her work, those few who exhibit resilience in the face of adversity—those willing to negotiate and realign their expectations for happiness—often discover a kind of contentment. Perhaps the most telling example of this kind of adaptation in Thompson's work is the love affair (in her novel *The Year We Left Home*) between an artist who starts his life with no advantages and a woman who, after suffering a debilitating and life-changing stroke as a teenager, goes on to become an accomplished and committed art photographer. These unlikely characters meet through their mutual connection to a deeply damaged Vietnam vet who serves as a kind of trickster figure throughout the novel. Together, the three of them form a new kind of family, which, although imperfect and limited, nonetheless deepens their individual humanity and allows all of them to live with greater dignity than they would if alone. Such arrangements, Thompson seems to be saying in many of her novels and stories, are as much as any of us can expect from life, and they are often the basis for a deeper form of happiness than that celebrated by the dominant culture.

Thompson elaborates on this theme in her most recent novel, *The Humanity Project,* which is in part the story of a wealthy, dotty woman who creates a foundation dedicated to the promotion of happiness. Perhaps unsurprisingly, little is achieved by the foundation itself, but the bonds formed between the individuals within the inner circle of the foundation's project become the real story. Despite the problem of human nature, real relationships, flawed as they may be—in this novel, and in all of Jean Thompson's work—are the truest route to a modest sort of happiness.

Ladette Randolph is the editor-in-chief of Ploughshares.

WELCOME TO HELL
A Plan B Essay by Jesse Lee Kercheval

In the Plan B essay series, writers discuss their contingency plans, extraliterary passions, and the roads not traveled.

The way my husband tells the story, I slipped on the ice, got a concussion, and when I woke up, said, "I want to learn to play the accordion." It is true that, after a concussion, I e-mailed my friends who were musical, asking if anyone had an accordion I could borrow. I wanted to try one out. I remember this process as being rather more logical than my husband's story, but I could be wrong. I wanted something portable. Something musical that had buttons or keys like a computer, not something as daunting as the violin, which my daughter plays, where your fingers only know where to be because your ear tells them. My entire lifelong experience with music was a year of halfhearted piano lessons when I was six. I wasn't sure I had an ear.

A friend replied to my e-mail, asking if anyone had an accordion, with "You're kidding, right?" Because, it turns out, her husband, Will, has uncounted number of accordions, six in her living room alone, a room I have been in countless times. This is my new realization. Life is full of accordions. I couldn't see them before, but now, magically, they are everywhere. Will said he would be happy to lend me an accordion.

The first thing Will asked me was what kind of music I wanted to play. I honestly had no idea. I was born in France and had a vague image of the kind of *bal musette* music, sad, wet, weepy, played in cellar cafés in old French movies. I imagined myself in a beret, with a cigarette dangling from my lip. OK, he said, for French music you need a G/C. He picked one accordion off the shelf. It was in a case about the size of an old-fashioned record player. He opened it and pulled out a small rectangular instrument, black wood with gold trim. It had buttons, not keys. On one side were twenty-one buttons. On the other, eight. It was a Hohner Pokerwork. A good accordion for a beginner, Will assured me. He showed me how to hold the accordion, how to play a C scale. He played by ear. I would learn to pick out tunes, he said.

He found his way into a few, apologizing as he did, saying he played mostly Irish music on a B/C accordion and the layout was completely different. I nodded as if I understood. He warmed up and began playing so fast—jigs, reels—his fingers blurred. At the end of half an hour or so, I thanked him. He put the accordion back in its case and handed it to me. See how you like it. We shook hands.

I brought the accordion home. I really had no idea how to play it. It turned out I had been right. I had no ear at all. I couldn't think of a tune, not even "Mary Had a Little Lamb," and then find the notes. So I Googled "How to play a button accordion" and was rewarded with dozens of sites and thousands of videos. So I set out to learn what I thought of as a decidedly old-world instrument in the new world wide web way.

"Good thing we're the landlords," my husband said, joking. He wasn't the only one. After I started noticing that accordions are everywhere, I noticed accordion jokes are too. The most famous is a cartoon by Gary Larson. People lined up on a cloud are welcomed by an archangel who says "Welcome to Heaven…Here's your harp." Down below, a line is greeted by a devil who says, "Welcome to Hell…Here's your accordion." Still, I happily spent hours playing, until the odd fact that the same button makes one note when you pull the bellows and another when you push became second nature to me. Like breathing in, then breathing out.

On YouTube, I watched Argentines playing tango accordions (as well as bandoneons), Austrians schrammelmusik on schrammel-harmonikas, Brazilians forró on their accordions, Chileans cumbia and vallenato, Dominicans merengue, Eastern European Jews klezmer music, Egyptians baladi, Greeks rebetiko, Italians tarantellas, Mexicans Norteño, and Basques squeezing their trikitixas—the list goes on. Cheap, portable, nearly every nation on the globe has taken the accordion as their own. Once I looked, I saw accordions everywhere in the indie rock world as well—The Decemberists, Beirut, The Magnetic Fields. I settled on the music of Brittany, ancestral home of the Kerchevals, with its sad Celtic tunes. I practiced and practiced.

And it worked. I got better. When I played the Hohner Pokerwork, first my dog and then my family stopped fleeing the house. A statement that is both true and, at least partly, an accordion joke.

Jesse Lee Kercheval was born in France and raised in Florida. She is the author of twelve books including the novel My Life as a Silent Movie *(Indiana University Press, 2013) and the memoir* Space *(Algonquin Books, 1998), which will be reissued by University of Wisconsin Press this spring.*

CHESSBOARD & CORNUCOPIA:
FORTY YEARS OF *INVISIBLE CITIES*
A Look2 Essay by John Domini

As you head south and east, with your back to the sea, the city of Alvito draws you uphill along ever-smaller roads, tightening spirals and switchbacks that soon have you confused over what's the approach and what the close-clustered town itself. Around just which curb-hugging rise and turn did you finally arrive? Nothing so defines this metropolis as its precipitousness...

The above concerns an actual place, about an hour outside Rome, a "city" insofar as it's defined by culture and close living quarters. The *style* of my description, however, the parody I'm attempting—respectfully—that's what Americans will recognize before they think of any Italian reality. It's the style of *Invisible Cities,* of the cities within *Cities.*

Fifty-five thumbnails, the longest a few pages, the shortest half a page, take up most of Italo Calvino's slim text and supply its defining innovation. Indeed, their bulk proves *part* of the innovation. Plenty of writers had set fictions in fantasy downtowns, but none had dreamed up so many at once. One metropolis in the 1974 novel comes alive as a memory of young love; another presents faces of the unhappy dead. One hangs in hammocks, another stands on stalks, another contains a museum of its own ideal forms, forever perfect, and another remains eternally unfinished, nothing but abandoned plumbing. Each miniature is rendered with improbable specificity, in bits and pieces now exotic, now mundane. Each brings off a small tale of discovery, a bracing single shot of narrative.

Sets of ten cities open and close the book, and these bracket seven sets of five, but enclosing the whole there's another sort of bracket. There's a sketch of a story connecting the city sketches. Marco Polo, footloose merchant, shares his travels with the stay-at-home emperor Kublai Khan. This frame device turns out to be itself about framing, since the Khan seeks a better sense of his domains: "to discern," as the novel's opening has it, "through the walls and towers destined to crumble, the tracery of a pattern so subtle it could escape the termites' gnawing." This premise alone sets *Invisible Cities* far beyond ordinary storytelling. Still, nothing's so striking as the cities themselves, a Baedeker unparalleled in its variety, forever playing peekaboo with pattern: now you see one, now you don't.

And this game has continued for forty years. First publication came at the end of 1972, and hardly eighteen months later arrived the English translation, the pinnacle of William Weaver's career, scrupulous yet songlike. By the end of the first print run, American novelists as far apart as John Barth and Gore Vidal were hailing Calvino an international grandmaster, beside the likes of Grass, Naipaul, or Garcia Marquez.

Those reputations, however, are based in the tradition of the social novel. *A House for Mr. Biswas,* for instance, generates story out of well-known tensions. It's about race, colonialism, and money-grubbing, and while the narrative includes a touch of formal experiment, its primary task remains to embody a place and a people. *Cities,* on the other hand, tends to *dis*embody. Merchant and emperor do without psychological backing and filling, and their dialogue makes no pretense to the ring of the street. The two men scuffle toward the end, but their pushing and shoving may take place only in dream, and after that the frame tale itself is rendered irrelevant. It turns out that the emperor has an atlas. Throughout, too, in place of rising action, Calvino has rising numbers. His cities are presented according to the Fibonacci series, a mathematical pattern rich in suggestion—though one that remains largely undiscussed by fans and celebrants.

Granted, the meditations on cities eventually develop a resonance within the world we know. The final ten towns include Procopia, where a population explosion crowds the view with "an expanse of faces..." (an image that also suggests the proliferation of media), and Penthesilea, which has no center, only endless sprawl, "one limbo [after] another." Many critics have noted these nightmares of collapse, and the way they build to Polo's closing, a plea for the livable city. We must give space, the traveler warns, to what is "not inferno." Yet as Calvino's twentieth century recedes, his foremost accomplishment hardly looms as a contribution to urban studies. Rather, *Cities* has become a benchmark for narrative.

William Gass, in an encomium that rolls on like a caravan, struggles to place the book in some alternative genre. He settles for "one of the purer works of the imagination," and indeed, placed alongside *Invisible Cities,* other recent achievements in the long story can look adulterated.

Even *Infinite Jest* or *The Elementary Particles* at once reveal their debt to classics of the form. Not surprisingly, then, the last four decades have seen more and more authors trying to steer by this willowy new landmark. More and more, book-length fiction has taken the form of variations on a theme, in which the consistency of a motif matters more than the depth of a character. The model proved especially congenial for Gilbert Sorrentino, in his last novels, but a better-known case would be Zachary Mason's *The Lost Books of the Odyssey*. Mason's debt to *Cities* was especially clear in the original, on Starcherone Press, which included a frame tale excised for big-house publication. Indeed, cuttings off Calvino's rootstock flourish on the smaller indies; an exemplary case would be Matt Bell's *Cataclysm Baby*, but the approach doesn't exclude best sellers either. Alan Lightman's *Einstein's Dreams* and David Eagleman's *Sum* are pop confections whipped up *Cities*-style, substituting comfy metaphysics for urban rough edges.

Other authors have left their stamp on the art form, to be sure. Garcia Marquez introduced a contagious strain of magic, and no doubt we'll soon see knockoffs of Thomas Bernhard's hundred-page paragraphs, all bile and erudition. Still, the nearest analogue I can see to what Calvino did for the novel is what Beckett did for theater, in the decades after he stripped it down to rags.

> *Nothing so defines this metropolis as its precipitousness. Through-out Alvito, homes hundreds of years old stagger upslope and down, each striving to boost itself above or between the others, and yet the stone-bound claustrophobia of these palazzi and the winding stairs at their feet will open up, with a step onto a balcony, at a turn in the stair, to airy vistas of the farm plains—green, black, dappled, dun—far below. At a glance the gritty and fecund stacks of basaltic rock fall away, and you could be a hawk, idling spread-winged and scouring the fields for prey...*

Another measure of the novel's impact is how often it brought the author to the US. Back in 1960, Calvino had swung through the States on a Ford Foundation grant, but this was for his work as an editor. He'd championed exchanges across the Iron Curtain and overseen major translations (among Americans, Bernard Malamud). His creative output kept pace, though, starting with *The Path to the Nest of Spiders* in '47. This debut verges on the surreal, and has traces of fable, yet it's a war novel; it draws on Calvino's time with the guerrillas of northern Italy, combat that left him, he later claimed, "an unparalleled sense of the human." Still it took *Invisible Cities,* Calvino's tenth or eleventh work of fiction (depending...), to make him a Distinguished Visiting Writer. Barth, at Johns Hopkins, arranged the first visit early in '76. After that, for the nine years left to him, Calvino came over often. The project on his desk at his death—not yet 62, multitasking as ever, and smoking, smoking—was a series of lectures to be delivered at Harvard.

These were *Six Memos for the New Millennium,* something of an aesthetic manifesto, but concerning *Invisible Cities* the author's nearest thing to full disclosure came in the spring of '83, at Columbia. The talk is difficult to find in English, but it's transcribed in the Italian critical edition of *Cities.* The sentences, despite their everyday vocabulary, coil something like those in the novel. Calvino begins with his habit of keeping file folders of occasional reflections: "a folder for objects, a folder for animals...one for historical figures, one for heroes of myth..." Whenever a folder grew full, his job became "to think of the book [he] could pull out of it," and as the 1960s ended, his fattest folders had to do with cities.

The decade had begun with the American visit, and in a letter home he claimed he wanted his tombstone to read "*newyorkese.*" In Italy, he bounced from Turin to Rome to smaller centers like Alvito, trips abroad included Tripoli and Havana, and in '67 he settled in Paris. On an earlier visit, he'd met his wife, the woman he called Chichita, a multilingual Argentine Jew whose actual name was Esther, and the year following the relocation, as a wave of youth revolt shook cities everywhere, the worst upheavals came in his new home. Rioters pried the stones from the streets and chanted *La vie est ailleurs,* "Life is elsewhere."

Amid this turmoil, Calvino's folders began to reflect both the actual and the elsewhere. One collected places he'd known, "life-passages for me," while another held cities of the imagination. Together these "became a diary that traced [his] moods," now a metropolis like "a sky full of stars" and now nothing but "garbage." Everything in his experience ended up in "images of cities," and "carried along behind," he sought to discern the tracery of a pattern.

A creative spirit so restless as Calvino's could never settle for memoir. Rather he began to sort his notes in groupings that, nearly half a century later, remain familiar: *Cities & Memory, Cities & Desire*... These first two he knew to be "fundamental," but another of his initial attempts at categorization, *Cities & the Form,* he rejected as "generic." He preferred the concrete, such as *Cities & Eyes,* and he didn't want the text's *percorso,* its way home, "completely disconnected" from his original, more personal order. By the time he developed his *Hidden* and *Continuing* sets, the author was working "*apposta,*" deliberately building on the form he'd glimpsed first in the juxtaposition of memory and desire. Polo and Khan emerged as a natural complement, another set of contraries, in an initial lump of "material," which Calvino then dispersed among the rest, "each to its own part." Polo's thirteenth-century *Travels,* after all, is known in Italian as *Il Milione,* "the million," for the number of lies it's supposed to contain, and for a certain sort of novelist this very quality made the text accommodating: "an imaginary continent in which other literary works find space."

Finding space, in the '83 talk at Columbia, also comes to mean finding a direction. The percorso proved central to the creative act:

> A book...is a space in which a reader can enter, turn about, perhaps lose himself, but at a certain point find an exit...Some of you may tell me that this definition better suits a novel of plot, and not a book like this...All right, but I would claim that also a work like this, in order to be a book, must have a certain construction, in which it's possible to discover a plot, an itinerary, a resolution.

As for that word *plot,* remarkable under the circumstances, the Italian is *intreccio,* which also translates as "weave" and "nest." Out of gleanings from what he'd known, what he still wished for, and what he saw under threat around him, the peripatetic magpie Calvino wove a new home for his imagination.

At a glance the gritty and fecund stacks of basaltic rock fall away, and you could be a hawk, idling spread-winged and scouring the fields for prey. No scrambling small rodent below, however, is quite so helpless as the farmer. His parcels of orchard and vineyard and eggplant, which once rolled on for miles beneath the city, keep collapsing together into consolidated holdings. Agribusiness in its far-off capitals, casting its web of finance models, demands ever more systematized growing cycles, more single-crop dependency. And with each fresh demand, another family farmer abandons what was once the far-flung ducal territory of Alvito, and with those farmers there disappear folks from the city, their own livings dependent, one way or the other, on the valley's former diverse haul, here olives, there truffles, there pig. The locals can no longer cling to the mountainside; the gravity proves too much.

What then is this "itinerary"? The author was uncomfortable with the way critics reduced the text to Polo's final admonition. To protect what's "not inferno," to Save the City: even William Gass treats this as the book's ruling purpose. Yet for an argument like that, wouldn't we do better to read Jane Jacobs? *The Death and Life of Great American Cities?* Worries about our disappearing downtowns, our degraded quality of life, go back considerably further than the Paris riots, and Calvino himself, during his Columbia talk, argues that his work is something else, "polyhedral." He claims that "all its folds" offer potential concluding insights, "no less epigrammatic." He wraps up his remarks by pointing to Chapter Five, "the heart of the book," where he locates "a theme of lightness, strange in its association with the theme of cities."

Lightness is a cardinal virtue for this author, one of those upheld in *Six Memos;* and in *Cities,* it's a sylphlike set of five he singles out. The chapter includes Octavia, dangling on webs above an abyss, and Baucis, standing on "long flamingo legs." One city, Leandra, comes close to holding a mirror to nature, its political squabbles sound familiar, but they're the nattering of fairy folk. Chapter Five is introduced, moreover, by Kublai's dreams of "cities light as kites…cities like leaves' veins." When he wakes, he hears of a town with "slender pinnacles, made in such a way that the moon in her journey can rest now on one, now on another."

A lovely fancy—but one Calvino had imagined before. Over the decade preceding *Cities,* he produced a number of titles, but most collected odds and ends; in '68 he not only refused an award for one, *t zero,* but also asked that his name be withdrawn from all other award considerations. The only recent work that mattered to him seemed to be the '65 story sequence *Cosmicomics*. In that book, "The Distance of the Moon" brings off a similar biplay between planet and satellite. At one point, the moon sways atop a pole, and the touch is made poignant, part of a bravura narrative of adultery, night-sea voyages, and gathering the lunar cheese.

Narrative rules in *Cosmicomics*: the fictions demonstrate expert command of situation, complication, and climax, all the more impressive given their material. *'Comics* has even less recognizable reality to work with than *Cities*. Stories consider the beginning of the universe, the formation of the galaxies, and the Big Bang itself. The narrator in every case is some particle of Essence that's been around eternally. Yet his tales render Freytag's Triangle with such dash that two appeared in *Playboy* (pieces devoid of sex, I should add) and the first US edition, in '68, was labeled "Science Fiction." Now, still, some Calvino readers prefer *Cosmicomics* to *Cities*. Others point back to another triumph of story over situation, namely, *The Baron in the Trees*, from 1957. *Baron* concerns an eighteenth-century aristocrat who moves out of the manor and up into the trees. His arboreal travels at times anticipate Polo's, and weave an *intreccio* in which the Enlightenment arrives at the point of a bayonet and a love affair tumbles with the beauty of a November leaf.

In all the work back to *Nest of Spiders*, Calvino's allegiance was to *both* wild ingenuity and story satisfaction. In the process, he could raise philosophical issues, in particular issues of the good society (in *Baron* especially) but these worked through conflict to a dramatic resolution. This author had earned the authority to claim that a book should have "an itinerary, a plot." Still, by his early forties, the later 1960s, his sensibility had grown restive.

He married and left Italy, but as he reveals in the rueful *Hermit in Paris,* the move never generated that "inner landscape for the imagination to...turn into its theater." His introduction to the City of Light had been the cracking yarns of the Musketeers, but to live there reduced the place to "a series of practical problems." So, too, in *Cities,* again about midway along, the glory of Phyllis dwindles to "a door here, a stairway there, a bench where you can put down your basket." The author needed more, new material for the interior theater, and as he and his wife worked on a translation of Raymond Queneau, Calvino entered the French author's salon—his "workshop for potential literature," Oulipo.

The relationship with Oulipo can be seen as symbiotic: the group enabled Calvino's break from story, and he brought them greater stature. *Invisible Cities* was his first wholly new work out of the affiliation, and no other title linked with the salon (such as Georges Perec's *A Void*) enjoys anywhere near its esteem and influence. *The Oulipo Compendium,* put together by Harry Mathews, certainly includes numbers-based exercises, suggesting what Calvino does with the Fibonacci series. Certainly, by the mid-'70s the author was into a fresh series of texts, all original and coherent, and all radical breaks from narrative. The best known, *If on a Winter's Night a Traveler* (English, 1981), proceeds by first setting up intrigues not unlike those that sustain the earlier works—steep, strange challenges—and then cutting them off.

Still, the shift in aesthetic had to do with a lot besides Oulipo. The Italian, the hermit in Paris, wasn't an active participant. He'd begun exploring writers like Queneau long before, and during this same period, his reading often took him in the opposite direction, to the ancient forms of fable and fairytale. Starting in 1970, he edited collections of the Brothers Grimm and others, writing several prefaces. The best-known is his *Italian Folktales* (English, 1990), praised by the arch-conservative John Gardner. The power of *Cities,* in other words, was forged in a tension between old pleasures of the text and a recognition that those pleasures no longer suited his energies. The percorso he'd always followed had reached a dead end.

Locals in Alvito can no longer cling to the mountainside; the gravity proves too powerful. Along the city's byways, there tends not to echo a clippity-clop but a schlip-schlip-schlip, as only the old shuffle by. More and more, a palazzo's double doors, wide enough to welcome a carriage, thick enough to absorb a musket ball, depend on a heavy padlock to hold them in place. Archways sprout weeds in the mornings, bats in the evening, and even the castle on the mountaintop doesn't so much crown the little metropolis as offer a way station up the slope toward the ghost town: the gloom just overhead. Small wonder that lovers can't get enough of the place. Small wonder that no sooner does the light start to fail than the cars rise grumbling into the disused centro, with two to every car, and a fair number of the Fiats and Audis borrowed from a friend in order to escape detection.

The lightness of *Cities,* in short, must never be mistaken for fluff. Its cloud castles are streaked with storm; the plea to hold off the inferno should be taken also as a stay against creative failure, and rickety, on stilts. This quality again recalls Beckett, his long shelf of last words, but Calvino has none of Beckett's austerity. Each cup of city arrives brimming, even the cemetery-town Agria. Most offer a taste of the freshly made, a display of the Baroque, or—the most common refreshment—some inkling of a lover. Sensuality occurs in such variety, it can't help but suggest the author's homeland, and no doubt he suffered the absence, at his desk in Paris. The book he pulled from his folders emphasized, above all, two aspects of *Italianità.*

The first is the Fibonacci series, where each term is the sum of the previous two in the series. The opening (0, 1, 0+1=1, 1+1=2, 1+2=3, 2+3=5…) provides the sequence for the sets of cities. Their stagger-step up to five and down follows a pattern scientists know as the Golden Ratio, because it occurs in many natural forms, from the uncoiling of a snail shell to the clustering of sunflower seeds. Of course, to test the ratio required technology far beyond that of Fibonacci himself, a twelfth-century mathematician out of Pisa (a contemporary, that is, of Marco Polo's father). Still, his figures have proved correct, placing most flora and fauna on a grid—or a chessboard, to use a recurring image from *Cities.* The board, of course, belongs to the Khan, "a keen… player," who believes that winning at chess will allow him to "finally possess [his] empire." As the novel arrives at what would ordinarily serve as the climax point (the eighth chapter of nine), Kublai orders Polo to stay at the palace and play. Far-fetched travelogues will profit the emperor less than mastering the game. But the hours over the board leave him in crisis, his values bankrupt:

> Each game ends in a gain or a loss: but of what? …At checkmate, beneath the foot of the king, knocked aside by the winner's hand, a black or white square remains… [T]he empire's multiform treasures were only illusory envelopes…

Illusory forms, empty, as if the scent and hue of a flowerbed, its spices and thorns, were reduced to the numbers game of some old Italian. The bleak vision suggests as well an artist's despair, when inspiration goes lifeless, and consequently no moment in *Invisible*

Cities feels so heartening as when Polo, in the closing frame of this same "climax" (the chapter's closing dialogue), begins to refill the envelopes. Where the Khan saw scorched earth, his guest envisions a garden: "Your chessboard, sire, is inlaid with two woods: ebony and maple." The Venetian reseeds the barren black and white; he imagines buds, larvae, woodsmen, and the artisan at his lathe. In no time Kublai is left "overwhelmed," his senses reawakened by "rafts laden with logs…women at the windows…"

In this exchange resides the essential dialectic of the text, between Form and Content. The Emperor sits alert to any sign of a controlling pattern, believing that "on the day when I have learned the rules, I shall finally possess my empire," and the merchant comes and goes, toting an ever-changing urban cornucopia. It's Polo who spies a woman in what was, a moment before, a rectangle in a blank wall. The Venetian plays the hero, you could say, since he gets the final, restorative word, both at the (surrogate) climax and the (sort of) conclusion; he provides a happy ending, you could say. Indeed, John Updike dubbed Calvino "the sunniest" of twentieth-century fabulists, in his review of *Cities*. Yet while the compliment's not out of line, it's over-simple. This novel can't be read like some episode of *Star Trek: TNG*, in which sloppy humanity defeats the regimented Borg.

Only an Emperor of Forms, after all, could supply the Fibonacci stutter-step, a ratio one also detects in chess combinations. The sequence propels our reading, a timekeeper, like the threes and nines in Dante's *Divine Comedy*. Besides that, at another fold in the book's middle, it's the Khan who intuits how Venice informs all of Polo's fabulations. The voyager's "first city" is "implicit" in them all, and the insight proves sharp enough to set the merchant doubting his goods: "perhaps, speaking of other cities, I have already lost [Venice], little by little." It's a moment when Content comes out the loser, in the biplay—and when Kublai stands in for a good reader, who senses Calvino's doubt and fears. Then there's the great irony of the Khan's atlas. This last surprise reveals actual cities ("Granada, the streaked pearl of the caliphs; Lübeck, the neat, boreal port") and creates further ambiguity: "Your atlas preserves the differences intact: that assortment of qualities which are like the letters in a name." To suggest paradise and inferno are merely tricks of the alphabet undercuts Polo's dominance of the closing; it maintains the essential tension.

Calvino's task entails a rigor far beyond that of any earlier book of lists. Old Possum's charming *Practical Cats,* Bierce's snarky *Devil's Dictionary,* have nothing like this text's accumulative power. Still, in the end, appreciation of *Cities* must return to the cities, their serendipity and brio. It's a city that best exemplifies the second element crucial to the book's continuing enchantment.

Pyrrha, No. 3 of the "Cities & Names," comes roughly at midpoint— that again. Polo admits that years went by before he visited, but over that time he'd "conjured" it "through its name." He'd done the same with others: "Euphrasia, Odile, Margara, Getullia." Thus the narrative of his visit explores how the actual place supplanted "everything [he] had imagined." It's all mills, Pyrrha, including windmills, and these recall another wayfarer who didn't know what he was looking at. Like Quixote, Polo still sees a chimera, the city of his imagination. That place has lost its name, but it haunts the same crannies of the mind, "...a fragment or glimmer," and once more it calls up four odd names: "Euphrasia, Odile, Margara, Getullia."

The sojourn provides, first, yet another masterly miniature, evoking a subtlety of our inner life in a bit more than a page. What's more, that lingering glimmer of what we once believed illuminates, in this case, a dream lover. Odile would be the object of infatuation most English readers recognize, the trickster of *Swan Lake* (and by extension the prostitute Odette, from Proust, casting her spell over the well-born Swann). Also the names contain Shakespeare's Juliet, in Italian Giulietta; the girl was from Verona, after all. In that city, too, *Margara* echoes a common expression of regret, *magari,* "if only..." The word appears in a thousand love songs, and *Euphrasia* probably turns up in a couple as well, since in both Italian and English the term retains its Greek derivation, "an excess of happiness." More commonly, the word refers to an herb and its extract, eyebright. A few drops and you look as though you've been crying for joy.

Life is elsewhere, cried the rioters of Paris '68, but "elsewhere" often takes the form of a shadow-love. To settle down is a Pyrrhic victory; you win comfort and lose the dream. If you're a married man, no pairing's so natural as cities and desire. In Pyrrha the Ghost Lover may be only a "glimmer," but its gestures indicate, once again, the author, whose fiction began to find its new form when he was both a new husband (as of '64) and father ('65). After that he appears never to have strayed, but as a younger man he'd been active, in the style of other European intellectuals. Affairs included a movie actress and, according to his letters, "a sweet and embarrassing bigamy" in his twenties. Later, though happy with Chichita and his daughter, Calvino's work often had him traveling alone, and each new city must've raised, faintly, a siren call. Each allowed him to experience the paradox embodied by Isidora, one of the first visits in his developing text: a place where "desires are already memories." Hence the project that resulted wove together all his wandering, going back to his days as a guerrilla, in a vision of living arrangements constantly going to pieces, of "cities like leaves' veins." Our luck as readers depends on his exile: at every stop, he sensed his discoveries were at terrible risk, and he sketched each with awe, with love.

No sooner does the light start to fail than vehicles rise into the disused central square, always two to a vehicle, and sometimes in Fiats and Audis borrowed from a friend, in order to escape detection. After that, on benches of crumbling stone, before the view from Alvito's first plateau, couples nuzzle and coo beneath gargoyles, or what used to be gargoyles, before their teeth wore off, or before the monsters' faces were obscured by the smoke of the lovers' cigarettes, often enhanced with a smatter of hashish. More serious encounters, meanwhile, take place up along the spiral networks of alley and stair. There's always a door that's come off its hinges, and once inside, what do you need besides a blanket, a candle, a half bottle of booze or a smatter of hashish—what more, so long as love keeps you nubile and willing? The sighs and giggles, the chink of a belt buckle hitting the tile and murmurs of no, and no, and yes-s-s, these fill the shelves of the abandoned libraries, they echo like prayers through the deconsecrated chapels, imbuing all the moldering leftovers with such excitement as to seem the guiding purpose, the ultimate resolution, of the centuries upon centuries previous, with all their struggle and decay.

John Domini's essay will appear in his forthcoming selection, The Sea-God's Herb, *on Dzanc Books. Dzanc will also be bringing out his next book of stories,* MOVIEOLA! *He has three novels, other books, and a number of grants and awards. See johndomini.com.*

Alice Hoffman Prize for Fiction · Spring 2014

The Alice Hoffman Prize for Fiction *Ploughshares* is pleased to present Elise Juska with the third annual Alice Hoffman Prize for Fiction for her short story, "Transfer Station," which appeared in the Spring 2013 issue of *Ploughshares,* guest-edited by Major Jackson. The $1,000 award, given by acclaimed writer and *Ploughshares* advisory editor Alice Hoffman, honors the best piece of fiction published in the journal during the previous year.

About Elise Juska and "Transfer Station"

Elise Juska's new novel, *The Blessings,* is forthcoming in May from Grand Central Publishing and is a Barnes & Noble Discover Great New Writers selection for Summer 2014. Her short stories have appeared in *The Gettysburg Review, The Hudson Review, Salmagundi, Black Warrior Review, Harvard Review, The Missouri Review,* and elsewhere. She lives in Philadelphia, where she directs the undergraduate creative writing program at the University of the Arts.

What inspired "Transfer Station"?

This story grew out of observing a very specific moment: one of my mother's neighbors had been recently widowed and, several months after his wife died, I noticed he'd put a bunch of old furniture on his lawn. One day, while visiting my mom, I saw a carful of teenagers pull up to look at the furniture and excitedly load a coffee table into their trunk. I was struck by the exchange, the contents of one life transferred into another life: this grieving man—and the coffee table he and his wife had probably had for forty years—and these happy kids who had just scored free furniture for their dorm room. I tucked the moment away, and it was several months later that I began writing the story.

How did the story find its final form? What did you discover or grapple with while writing it?

The process of writing this story was somewhat unusual for me, so I remember it well. I wrote it almost entirely in Maine, on Orr's Island, where I've spent the last nine summers writing in a little cottage in the woods. I start early, around five or six, and write until late afternoon; almost without exception, I never write at night. The first draft of this story kept me up writing well past midnight, feeling tense and surprised and alarmed about what might happen when the kids entered Loring's house, a feeling I'm sure was only heightened by my solitude and surroundings.

In an early draft, the final scene went further—one of the kids resorted to beating up Loring—but it felt out of character for the kids and, ultimately, might have obscured the story's point. I wanted the final feeling to be bleak but also hopeful—Loring is losing things he loved deeply, but in so doing, is shocked into caring again about his life.

In creating these characters, my main concern was making sure they weren't too starkly bad or good; that is, while I certainly saw Loring as a sympathetic figure, I also wanted him to possess a slight sense of smugness or superiority. And the kids, while reckless and thoughtless, were also endearing to me in their insecure posturing.

How does this story fit with the rest of your work?

My writing often deals, in some way, with grief: how we manage it, tend to it, are paralyzed by or move through it. In my new novel, *The Blessings,* a death in a large family resonates through the lives of multiple characters over the next twenty years.

I'm also interested in the intersections among unlikely people, characters whose lives may seem dissimilar or disconnected; it's probably why the scene on my mother's neighbor's lawn stayed with me so strongly. Several of my recent stories have contained such moments, where a teacher or neighbor or relative stranger—or, here, three teenagers—ends up crossing paths with the main character, sometimes in a small way, and has an unexpectedly profound impact.

*Book Recommendations from
Our Advisory Editors*

Robert Boswell recommends *Cowboys and East Indians* by Nina McConigley: "This collection is full of lively, beautifully written stories about growing up in the American West as 'the wrong kind of Indian.' It is a wonderful addition to the literature of the West." (FiveChapters Books, September 2013)

B. H. Fairchild recommends *Curvature of a Fluid Spine* by Kenneth P. Gurney: "Self-published books of poetry have been the lost orphans of the poetry world for far too long, borne mostly of prolonged frustration with the mysteries of poetry competitions and arcane politics of literary publishing in general. Kenneth Gurney stood as one of the central figures in the New Mexico poetry scene for several years, with his work appearing regularly in scores of small magazines here and in the UK. Gurney is a skilled practitioner of classical free verse, acknowledging in the "Author's Note" his particular indebtedness to the work of Mary Ruefle. But his approach is entirely his own: astonishingly perceptive, Gurney reveals small moments of large import while balancing bursts of lyric spontaneity with unusually precise portraits of the natural world. This, combined with his nimble use of wit, allows his readers to locate light within apparent darkness. He should be read." (CreateSpace Independent Publishing Platform, March 2013)

David Gullette recommends *Bread on Running Waters* by Ani Gjika: "This is the first book of poems by Albanian American poet Ani Gjika. There's a mixture of strangeness and clarity in her vision, and the poems drawing on her Albanian childhood are particularly haunting. And yet Gjika is truly an American poet: her voice parallels that great American tradition of lyrical frankness. She is not to be missed." (Fenway Press, 2013)

DeWitt Henry recommends *The Wither'd Sedge* by Bruce Bennett: "In his latest collection, Bennett combines consummate craft, wit, and drama in a medley of love-gone-wrong songs that are reminiscent of Yeats, Housman, Frost, and, yes, Steve Martin's *The Lonely Guy*. Rue is framed by irony in this fresh collection." (Finishing Line Press, January 2014)

Tony Hoagland recommends *The Life and Ideas of James Hillman, Volume 1* by Dick Russell: "This is a fascinating intellectual biography that situates its readers directly inside the development of twentieth-century psychology. To read about what was going on at the Jung Institute in Zurich, 1953, is surprisingly exciting." (Arcade Publishing, June 2013)

Philip Levine recommends *Posthumous Poems* by Paul Petrie: "In his own modest introduction to this collection, Paul Petrie refers to himself as 'a very quirky individual,' and while he indeed may have been, this capacious final collection—assembled by the author but published after his death—proves that he was an enormously talented, mature writer of boundless energy and inspiration. Considering how little attention the public gave his work, Petrie's seventy-year commitment to poetry was both miraculous and heroic. He also tells us, in the introduction, that he had no pretensions to a consistent philosophy; in practice he took the world as it came to him in all its beauty and terror and transformed his own experiences into an astonishingly rich body of work. Like Theodore Roethke, he was able to move into any form that suited the occasion, traditional or experimental, and still maintain the unmistakable voice that marks the work as genuine. Even in the later poems there is a willingness to enter into the spirit of play and discover a kind of sanity beyond sanity. Poem after poem reveals the magic that pervades daily life, the transformations that are so common we've forgotten that they are part of us." (Antrim House, 2014)

Margot Livesey recommends *What Ends* by Andrew Ladd: "What a lovely writer Andrew Ladd is, and what a compelling novel he has written about the five members of the McCloud family and their island home of Eilean Fìor. Each of the McClouds is rendered with vivid complexity and it is that same clarity of detail that makes *What Ends* so suspenseful and so deeply satisfying. Surely every reader will want to visit Eilean Fìor; happily we can within these beautiful pages." (New Issues Poetry & Prose, January 2014)

Thomas Lux recommends *Chapel of Inadvertent Joy* by Jeffrey McDaniel: "McDaniel has extraordinary

metaphor-making abilities and his poems are as courageous as they come." (University of Pittsburgh Press, October 2013)

Campbell McGrath recommends *The Last Books of Héctor Viel Temperley* by Héctor Viel Temperley, translated by Stuart Krimko: "This amazing little book was published in 2011, bringing the work of this talented Argentinian poet to my attention for the first time. It comprises two long poems written in the years just before Viel Temperley's death in 1987, which are visionary, hallucinatory, and formally a unique mix of prose fragments, strophes, and imagistic lines. This collection is weird and astonishing in all the right ways." (Sand Paper Press, December 2011)

Dan Wakefield recommends *Leaving Little Havana* by Cecilia M. Fernandez: "This 'memoir of Miami's Cuban ghetto' is the first work I've seen that describes, in such vivid and compelling detail, the insular world of the Cuban refugees in Miami. Fernandez offers her own story as a child of one of the first 'waves' of Cubans to flee Castro's country and establish their own 'island in the city' with its own customs, politics, conflicts, and myths." (Beating Windward Press, January 2014)

Eleanor Wilner recommends *Without Angels* by Marjorie Stelmach: "Stelmach is a wise and seasoned poet who gives us a ravishing glimpse of our better angels as they depart; her scintillant language makes even the gathering dust of our days incandescent." (MayApple Press, March 2014)

Russell Banks, *A Permanent
Member of the Familiy,* stories
(Ecco, November 2014)

Anne Bernays, with Justin Kaplan,
*Back Then: Two Literary Lives in
1950s New York,* nonfiction (Harper-
Collins, December 2013)

Martín Espada, *The Meaning of the
Shovel,* poems (Smokestack Books,
January 2014)

Carolyn Forché, ed., with Duncan
Wu, *Poetry of Witness: The Tradition
in English, 1500-2001* (W. W. Norton,
January 2014)

Alice Hoffman, *The Museum of
Extraordinary Things,* a novel
(Scribner, February 2014)

Justin Kaplan, *Lincoln Steffens:
Portrait of a Great American
Journalist,* nonfiction (Simon &
Schuster, November 2013)

Bill Knott, *Collected Poetry 1960-
2014* (CreateSpace, January 2014)

Lorrie Moore, *Bark: Stories*
(Knopf, February 2014)

Antonya Nelson, *Funny Once:
Stories* (Bloomsbury USA,
May 2014)

Gary Soto, *Instant Winner,* audiobook and ebook (AudioGO,
December 2013)

Colm Tóibín, *The Testament of
Mary,* audiobook read by Meryl
Street (Simon & Schuster Audio,
September 2013)

Ellen Bryant Voigt, *Headwaters:
Poems* (W. W. Norton, October 2013)

Eleanor Wilner, ed., with Maurice
Manning, *The Rag-Picker's Guide
to Poetry: Poems, Poets, Process*
(University of Michigan Press,
November 2013)

CONTRIBUTORS' NOTES
Spring 2014

Erin Belieu's most recent book from
Copper Canyon Press, *Slant Six,* is
due in September 2014.

Malachi Black is the author of the
poetry collection *Storm Toward
Morning,* forthcoming fall 2014 from
Copper Canyon Press. His poems
have appeared in *AGNI, Boston
Review, Gulf Coast, Harvard Review,
Narrative, Poetry,* and *Southwest
Review,* among other journals, and
in several recent anthologies, in-
cluding *Before the Door of God: An
Anthology of Devotional Poetry* (Yale
University Press), *The Poet's Quest
for God* (Eyewear Publishing, UK),
and *Discoveries: New Writing from
The Iowa Review* (The Iowa Review).
He is the Creative Writing Fellow in
Poetry at Emory University.

Mark Brazaitis is the author of six
books, including *The Incurables:
Stories* (University of Notre
Dame Press, 2012), winner of the
2012 Richard Sullivan Prize, and

Julia & Rodrigo (Gival Press, 2013), winner of the 2012 Gival Press Novel Award. His writing has been featured on the Diane Rehm Show, as well as on public radio in Cleveland, Iowa City, New York City, and Pittsburgh. A former Peace Corps Volunteer, he is a professor of English and the director of the West Virginia Writers' Workshop at West Virginia University.

Dan Chaon is the author of the short-story collection *Stay Awake* (Ballantine Books, 2012), the novel *Await Your Reply* (Ballantine Books, 2009) and other works of fiction. He lives in Cleveland.

Kim Chinquee is the author of the collections *Oh Baby* (Ravenna Press, 2008), *Pretty* (White Pine Press, 2010), and *Pistol* (Ravenna Press, 2012). She is a frequent contributor to *NOON, Denver Quarterly,* and *Conjunctions,* and her work has appeared in other journals, such as *The Nation, The Huffington Post, Mississippi Review, Fiction,* and *BOMB.* She is the recipient of a Pushcart Prize and a Henfield Prize, is an associate editor of New World Writing, and chief editor of *ELJ (Elm Leaves Journal).* She lives and teaches in Buffalo, New York.

Jae Choi received her MFA from the Iowa Writers' Workshop. Her poems have appeared in *Tin House, The Iowa Review, Poor Claudia,* and other publications. She has taught poetry at Reed College and Portland State University. She lives in Los Angeles.

Stephen Dau is the author of *In a Foreign Country* (forthcoming) and *The Book of Jonas* (Blue Rider Press, 2012), which was a semifinalist for the Cabell First Novelist Award and was named one of the best books of the year by *Kirkus Reviews* and *Booklist.* He worked in postwar reconstruction and international philanthropy before receiving an MFA from the Bennington Writing Seminars. His work has been featured on *NPR* and appeared in *McSweeney's, Pittsburgh Post-Gazette,* and *MSNBC.* He lives in Belgium.

Alice Derry lives and works on Washington's Olympic Peninsula. *Tremolo,* her fourth volume of poetry, appeared from Red Hen Press in 2012. *Strangers to Their Courage* (Louisiana State University Press, 2001) was a finalist for the Washington State Book Award. Derry's first manuscript, *Stages of Twilight* (Far Corner Books, 1986), was chosen by Raymond Carver for publication. In May of 2013, she delivered the keynote address for his 75th Birthday Celebration in Port Angeles.

Denise Duhamel is the author, most recently, of *Blowout* (2013) *Ka-Ching!* (2009), *Two and Two* (2005), and *Queen for a Day: Selected and New Poems* (2001), all from the University of Pittsburgh Press. The guest editor for *The Best American Poetry 2013,* she teaches at Florida International University in Miami.

Elizabeth Evans is the author of five books, including *Suicide's Girlfriend* (Harper Perennial, 2002) and *Carter*

Clay (Harper Perennial, 2000). A new novel, *As Good as Dead*, is forthcoming from Bloomsbury. Evans' awards include the Iowa Author Award, a National Endowment for the Arts Fellowship, the James Michener Fellowship, a Lila Wallace Award, and residencies at MacDowell Colony, Yaddo, and other foundations. She is Professor of Creative Writing at University of Arizona and makes her home in Tucson.

Rebecca Morgan Frank is the author of *Little Murders Everywhere* (Salmon Poetry, 2012), a finalist for the Kate Tufts Discovery Award, and she received the Poetry Society of America's Alice Fay di Castagnola Award for her new manuscript-in-progress. She is cofounder and editor of the online magazine *Memorious*, and she teaches at the University of Southern Mississippi's Center for Writers.

Jennifer Haigh is the author of the story collection *News From Heaven* (Harper Perennial, 2014) and four critically acclaimed novels: *Faith* (HarperCollins, 2011), *The Condition* (HarperCollins, 2008), *Baker Towers* (William Morrow, 2005), and *Mrs. Kimble* (William Morrow, 2003). Her books have won both the PEN/Hemingway Foundation Award for debut fiction and the L.L. Winship/PEN New England Award, and have been published in nineteen languages. Her short stories have appeared in T*he Atlantic, Granta, The Best American Short Stories* and many other publications. She lives in Boston.

Robert Hellenga has published a dozen short stories in literary magazines. His first novel, *The Sixteen Pleasures* (Soho Press, 1994), which became a national bestseller after being rejected 39 times, has recently been issued as an audio book (Blackstone Audio, Inc., 2013). His most recent novel, *Snakewoman of Little Egypt* (Bloomsbury USA, 2010) was named one of the best novels of 2010 by both the *Washington Post* and *Kirkus Reviews*. His seventh novel, *The Confessions of Frances Godwin*, will be published by Bloomsbury in summer 2014.

Rick Hilles is the author of *Brother Salvage* (University of Pittsburgh Press, 2006), winner of the 2005 Agnes Lynch Starrett Poetry Prize and named the 2006 Poetry Book of the Year by *ForeWord Reviews*, and *A Map of the Lost World* (University of Pittsburgh Press, 2012). He has been the recipient of a Whiting Writers' Award, the Amy Lowell Poetry Travelling Scholarship, a Camargo Foundation Fellowship, and an Individual Artist Fellowship from the Tennessee Arts Commission. An assistant professor of English at Vanderbilt University, he lives in Nashville, Tennessee.

Jesse Lee Kercheval was born in France and raised in Florida. She is the author of twelve books including the novel *My Life as a Silent Movie* (Indiana University Press, 2013) and the memoir *Space* (Algonquin Books, 1998), which will be reissued by University of Wisconsin Press this spring.

James Kimbrell is the author of *The Gatehouse Heaven* (1998) and *My*

Psychic (2006), both from Sarabande Books. His new collection of poetry, *Smote*, will be published by Sarabande in October 2015. His work has appeared in *Poetry, Narrative, The Cincinnati Review, The New Guard,* and *Best American Poetry 2012.* The recipient of a "Discovery"/The Nation Award, a Whiting Writer's Award, and *Poetry*'s Bess Hokin Prize, he currently directs the creative writing program at Florida State University.

Kent Leatham is a poet and translator. His work has appeared in dozens of journals, including *Fence, Poets & Artists, Poetry Quarterly, InTranslation,* and *SOFTBLOW,* as well as the 2013 Montreal Poetry Prize Global Anthology. Kent holds an MFA from Emerson College, and has taught at California State University Monterey Bay and served as a poetry editor for Black Lawrence Press. He lives on the central coast of California.

Elizabeth McCracken is the author of two novels, a memoir, and two collections of short stories, including *Thunderstruck & Other Stories* (The Dial Press, 2014). She teaches writing at the University of Texas, Austin.

Karyna McGlynn is the author of *I Have to Go Back to 1994 and Kill a Girl* (Sarabande Books, 2009), winner of the Kathryn A. Morton Prize, as well as two chapbooks. Her poems have recently appeared in *The Literary Review, Court Green, Salt Hill, West Branch, Subtropics,* and The Academy of American Poet's *Poem-A-Day.* Karyna received her MFA

from the University of Michigan, and is currently a PhD candidate in Literature & Creative Writing at the University of Houston. She is the managing editor of *Gulf Coast* and coordinator for the Houston Indie Book Festival and the Gulf Coast Reading Series.

Campbell McGrath is the author of nine books of poetry, most recently *In the Kingdom of the Sea Monkeys* (Ecco, 2012). He has received numerous awards, including a MacArthur Genius Fellowship, the Kingsley Tufts Poetry Award, a Ploughshares Cohen Award, a Guggenheim Fellowship, and a Witter-Bynner Fellowship from the Library of Congress. McGrath lives in Miami Beach with his wife and two sons and teaches in the MFA program at Florida International University.

Sarah Rose Nordgren is the author of *Best Bones,* winner of the Agnes Lynch Starret Poetry Prize, which is forthcoming from the University of Pittsburgh Press in fall 2014. Her poems have appeared or are forthcoming in *AGNI, 32 Poems, The Iowa Review, Pleiades, Harvard Review,* and the *Best New Poets* anthology. A two-time recipient of Provincetown's Fine Arts Work Center fellowship, Nordgren lives in Cincinnati, Ohio, and teaches at Miami University Middletown. For more information visit sarahrosenordgren.com.

Tatiana Oroño was born in San José, Uruguay, in 1947. She is the author of seven books, including *La Piedra Nada Sabe* (Estuario, 2008), *Morada móvil* (Artefato, 2004), and T*out fut ce qui ne fut pas/ Todo tuvo la forma que no tuvo* (Éscrits des Forges, 2002). Her poetry has been published in Argentina, Bolivia, Brazil, Canada, Cuba, Chile, El Salvador, Spain, France, Mexico, Puerto Rico, and the Dominican Republic.

Ben Purkert's poems have appeared in A*GNI, Fence, The Kenyon Review, The New Yorker,* and *Best New Poets 2012*. He is currently completing his first book. Find links to his work at benpurkert.com.

Peter Rock is the author of seven works of fiction, most recently *The Shelter Cycle* (Houghton Mifflin Harcourt, 2013) and *My Abandonment* (Houghton Mifflin Harcourt, 2009). "Go-Between" is part of a collaborative project that attempts to generate a fragmentary novel through interactions with the work of five photographers. The photo in the story is by Peter McCollough. This strategy was developed in the early '90s, while Rock was a security guard in an art museum. Born in Salt Lake City, Utah, he now lives in Portland, Oregon, with his wife, two fierce young daughters, and one sweet pit bull. For more information please visit peterrockproject.com.

Tony Sanders has published four collections of poetry, the fourth a collaboration with the poet Chard deNiord titled *Speaking in Turn* (Gnomon Press, 2012). His work has appeared in many journals, including *The Paris Review, The Yale Review, The New York Times Book Review,* and *Hotel Amerika.*

Jacob Sunderlin received an MFA from Purdue University and a poetry fellowship from the Fine Arts Work Center in Provincetown, Mass. His poetry appears or is forthcoming in *Colorado Review, Cream City Review, Cutbank, Forklift Ohio,* and elsewhere.

Donna Trump's work has been published in *Mid-American Review, Ars Medica,* and *Chautauqua,* among others. Her short story, "Wolf Notes," was nominated for a Pushcart Prize. Trump's education includes degrees in Biology and Physical Therapy and a host of writing classes taken and taught at The Loft Literary Center in Minneapolis. Honors include a Loft Mentorship with Sandy Benitez and Peter Ho Davies, a mentorship with Benjamin Percy, and a Minnesota Emerging Writers' Grant.

Ronald Wallace's twelve books of poetry, fiction, and criticism include *Long for This World* (2003) and *For a Limited Time Only* (2008), both from University of Pittsburgh Press. He is codirector of the program in creative writing at the University of Wisconsin-Madison and editor of the University of Wisconsin Press Poetry Series. He divides his time between Madison and a forty-acre farm in Bear Valley, Wisconsin.

Jonathan Wells' second collection *The Man With Many Pens* will be published by Four Way Books in 2016. His first collection *Train Dance* (Four Way Books) was published in 2011. His poems have appeared in *The New Yorker, Hayden's Ferry Review, Poetry International,* and many other places. He is a coeditor of the *Tebot Bach New World Translation Series* with Christopher Merrill and lives in New York.

Mike White's poems have appeared in magazines including *Poetry, The New Republic,* and *The Threepenny Review,* and online at *Poetry Daily* and *Verse Daily.* His first collection, *How to Make a Bird with Two Hands* (Word Works, 2012), received the 2011 Washington Prize. He lives in Salt Lake City and teaches at the University of Utah.

GUEST EDITOR POLICY

Ploughshares is published three times a year: mixed issues of poetry and prose in the spring and winter and a prose issue in the fall. The spring and fall issues are guest-edited by different writers of prominence, and winter issues are staff-edited. Guest editors are invited to solicit up to half of their issues, with the other half selected from unsolicited manuscripts screened for them by staff editors. This guest editor policy is designed to introduce readers to different literary circles and tastes, and to offer a fuller representation of the range and diversity of contemporary letters than would be possible with a single editorship. Yet, at the same time, we expect every issue to reflect our overall standards of literary excellence.

SUBMISSION POLICIES

We welcome unsolicited manuscripts from June 1 to January 15 (postmark dates). We also accept submissions online. Please see our website (pshares. org) for more information and guidelines. All submissions postmarked from January 16 to May 31 will be recycled. From March 1 to May 15, we also accept submissions online for our Emerging Writer's Contest.

Our backlog is unpredictable, and staff editors ultimately have the responsibility of determining for which editor a work is most appropriate. If a manuscript is not timely for one issue, it will be considered for another. Unsolicited work sent directly to a guest editor's home or office will be ignored and discarded.

All mailed manuscripts and correspondence regarding submissions should be accompanied by a self-addressed, stamped envelope (s.a.s.e.). No replies will be given by e-mail (exceptions are made for international submissions). Expect three to five months for a decision. We now receive well over a thousand manuscripts a month.

For stories and essays that are significantly longer than 5,000 words, we are now accepting submissions for *Ploughshares Solos* (formerly *Pshares Singles*), which will be published as e-books. Pieces for this series, which can be either fiction or nonfiction, can stretch to novella length and range from 6,000 to 25,000 words. The series is edited by Ladette Randolph, *Ploughshares* editor-in-chief.

Simultaneous submissions are amenable as long as they are indicated as such and we are notified immediately upon acceptance elsewhere. We do not reprint previously published work. Translations are welcome if permission has been granted. We cannot be responsible for delay, loss, or damage. Payment is upon publication: $25/printed page, $50 minimum and $250 maximum per author, with two copies of the issue and a one-year subscription. For *Ploughshares Solos,* payment is $250 for long stories and $500 for work that is closer to a novella. The prize for our Emerging Writer's Contest is $1,000 for the winner in each genre: fiction, poetry, and nonfiction.

BLACK WARRIOR REVIEW

Announcing the Tenth-Annual Contest for Fiction, Nonfiction, and Poetry!

Winners in each genre receive a $1,000 prize and publication in BWR 41.2, our Spring/Summer 2015 issue. Three runners-up will be awarded $100 in addition to publication. Each entry is $20 and comes with a one-year subscription to BWR.

Deadline: September 1, 2014.
For more information please visit bwr.ua.edu.

Salamander 2014 Fiction Prize
Final Judge: Jennifer Haigh
$1,500 Honorarium
and Publication

SEND ENTRIES FROM
MAY 15 THROUGH JUNE 15 TO:

2014 Fiction Prize
Salmander/Suffolk University
English Department
41 Temple Street • Boston, MA 02114
(or submit online)

Reading Fee:
(includes subscription) $15

• • •

For complete guidelines go to:
www.salamandermag.org

read. write. be read.

BENNINGTON COLLEGE
MASTER OF FINE ARTS IN WRITING

20 years
1994   2014
ALWAYS CURRENT. ALWAYS CLASSIC.

EMERGING WRITER'S CONTEST

POETRY • FICTION • NONFICTION

THE TRITON AMONG MINNOWS.
–The New York Times

In 1976, we discovered Tim O'Brien—at the time, an emerging writer. In 1980, we published the early work of Sue Miller, and in 1981, one of Edward P. Jones' first stories.

Since 2011, we have continued discovering great new writers via our Emerging Writer's Contest, open to all authors who have yet to publish a book.

HERE'S YOUR CHANCE TO BE DISCOVERED IN 2014!

The winner in each genre receives $1,000 and publication in *Ploughshares*. You can read the winning entries from the 2013 contest in this issue.

Our 2014 Emerging Writer's Contest opens on March 1st.

Break into one of America's best literary magazines, and get a one-year subscription or renewal with your $24 contest fee.

A NATIONAL TREASURE.
–Frank Conroy

SEE PSHARES.ORG/EMERGINGAWARD FOR DETAILS